MANAGEMENT OF
BRAIN DAMAGED CHILDREN

A Parents' and Teachers' Guide

MANAGEMENT OF BRAIN DAMAGED CHILDREN

A Parents' and Teachers' Guide

By

FRANCES G. BERKO, M.A., J.D.

Executive Director
Special Children's Center
Ithaca, New York

MARTIN J. BERKO, Ph.D.

Research Associate
Department of Psychology
Cornell University
Ithaca, New York

STEPHANIE C. THOMPSON, M.S.

Speech Therapist
Special Children's Center
Ithaca, New York

CHARLES C THOMAS • PUBLISHER

Springfield • Illinois • U.S.A.

Published and Distributed Throughout the World by

CHARLES C THOMAS • PUBLISHER

Bannerstone House

301-327 East Lawrence Avenue, Springfield, Illinois, U.S.A.

Natchez Plantation House

735 North Atlantic Boulevard, Fort Lauderdale, Florida, U.S.A.

*With THOMAS BOOKS careful attention is given to all details of
manufacturing and design. It is the Publisher's desire to present books that are
satisfactory as to their physical qualities and artistic possibilities and
appropriate for their particular use. THOMAS BOOKS will be true to those
laws of quality that assure a good name and good will.*

Printed in the United States of America
RV-1

PREFACE

THE problems associated with childhood brain damage have received a great deal of attention in the "professional" literature of the past twenty years. During this time, there have also been a small number of excellent "nonprofessional" books addressing discussions of some of these problems to parents of brain injured children and to similarly interested individuals. The senior authors of the present volume have long felt the need of an "intermediate" book in this area; that is, one whose informational content would be great enough so that it would be of value to physicians, psychologists, teachers, and other professionals who might have occasion to work with brain injured children, and yet a book containing practical, useful, straightforwardly presented guidance to parents and other persons having the day-to-day responsibility for the care and training of these youngsters. This proved to be a rather more difficult undertaking than we had anticipated, and one which we had put aside after several abortive attempts. Therefore we are grateful to our co-worker, Mrs. Stephanie Thompson, whose perseverance and ability to "find the right words" did so much to make the completion of this work possible.

The authors wish to express their thanks to Dr. Walter Carlin, Chairman, Department of Speech and Audiology at Ithaca College, under whom Mrs. Thompson did a graduate thesis which was the basis of a partial first draft of this book. Finally, we wish to express our gratitude to Dr. Merlin J. Mecham, Acting Chairman, Department of Speech, University of Utah. The senior authors worked with Dr. Mecham on the publication of two earlier books in this general area, and while he did not participate in the preparation of the present volume, his thinking and influence have undoubtedly found their way into many aspects of what is written therein.

Ithaca, New York   F.G.B.
                                                                                M.J.B.

CONTENTS

MANAGEMENT OF
BRAIN DAMAGED CHILDREN

A Parents' and Teachers' Guide

CHAPTER ONE

WHO IS THE BRAIN DAMAGED CHILD?

What the Brain Damaged Child is Like

MRS. Brown's pregnancy was normal until she went into premature labor eight weeks before the estimated delivery date. After a fast but somewhat difficult delivery, the baby had severe breathing difficulties and suffered lack of oxygen. He was placed in an incubator for a week and released from the hospital when he reached a weight of five pounds.

Despite his early difficulty, he appeared to develop normally during his first year of life, holding up his head, smiling, sitting, and so forth, at the normal ages. However, he was always a difficult baby, screaming, sleeping poorly, and not responding to his mother's attempts to soothe and comfort him. Cuddling and rocking didn't appear to calm him, and attempts to sing to him or talk to him did not help. In short, he was a "difficult baby to mother."

Johnny's development appeared to slow down after the first year. He didn't walk until age one and a half. At fourteen months, he said "mama" and "dada," but his speech progressed very little from that point. At age three, he spoke only ten words.

Johnny's behavior was a great problem for the family. He was demanding and had frequent outbursts of temper, especially when frustrated in his demands. He couldn't tolerate any disturbance in family routine or even slight disorder in the home. All doors had to be closed, his toys lined up in a certain way and the chairs in the house kept in the exact same positions at all times. If such dictates weren't followed, severe rage reactions would occur. His attention span was very short and he jumped from toy to toy and game to game all day. He was usually "all over the house and into everything." Johnny had always been a feeding problem, particularly from the time that solid food was added to his diet.

3

He refused to eat most foods that needed chewing and frequently gagged and choked on his food.

At age three, Johnny's behavior was characterized by frequent uncontrollable bursts of crying, screaming, and anger. He wasn't toilet trained, didn't dress himself, drooled continuously, and babbled and gestured, using very little actual speech.

The parents' attitude toward Johnny and his capabilities appeared to vacillate between extreme overprotection and underestimation of what he could do, and extreme overestimation of his potential. Areas in which he might succeed, such as self-help and toileting, were assumed to be "beyond him." Yet, when faced realistically with his failure to perform various tasks a child of his age could perform, the parents felt that he could do them "if he wanted to," but he didn't choose to do so.

From this picture, it is easy to see what difficulties can be encountered with a young, brain damaged child. Perhaps it will be even easier to visualize the problem of everyday living if we see just that — a typical day in the life of the child just described, prior to the family's acquisition of techniques of home management.

> Johnny woke fairly early in the morning and wanted his breakfast immediately. Any delay caused a severe emotional outburst. When breakfast was served, however, it caused arguments, as he refused foods requiring chewing, spilled his milk, fidgeted, tipped over his chair and so on.
>
> The next hurdle to be crossed was dressing. This was accomplished amidst great screaming, yelling, and kicking. It usually took both parents to dress Johnny; one holding him down and one stuffing him into his clothes. The chaos was added to by the presence of a younger sister, momentarily left to her own devices and upset by the noise so that she screamed in concert with her brother.
>
> From this point until lunch, Johnny was on a perpetual treadmill, jumping from activity to activity, racing around the house, getting into everything, and having frequent tantrums.
>
> Lunch was a repetition of breakfast. After a long nap, the afternoon progressed in much the same way as the morning. Each diaper change was a major battle, now to be fought single-handedly by the mother, with no extra hands to anchor Johnny to the changing table.
>
> When the father arrived home, he attempted to play with Johnny but usually overestimated the child's ability. This led to more

frustration for Johnny, another tantrum, and the father's feeling of failure and rejection by his son. After fighting through dinner, Johnny had to be undressed and put to bed. This usually was as wearing as the opposite procedure in the morning.

Obviously, a day characterized by battles such as these was exhausting for both Johnny and his parents, physically and emotionally. There was little if any opportunity for parents and child to enjoy each other. An attitude of tension pervaded the house, and all interactions between parents and child were shadowed with the expectation of impending crisis. A situation like this changes the normal give-and-take, easy-going, affectionate nature of a home into the wire tautness of a militarized zone.

We have just described what might be called the "typical" brain damaged child. However, it is practically a contradiction in terms to speak of anything typical in childhood brain damage. Other types of infancy and early childhood experiences are common also.

In some cases, rather than the markedly irritable baby and overactive toddler discussed above, the brain damaged infant may be the one described as "such a good baby." Such an infant is less responsive to the world around him and much more passive than normal babies. He is the infant who is content to be in his crib or playpen nearly all day and requires little attention from his parents.

This baby is often slow in developing: creeping, crawling, walking, and talking later than the norms parents read of in Spock or Gesell. The anxious mother may question her doctor, her friends, or her relatives, wondering why her son isn't walking yet, although he is fourteen months old, or why he hasn't yet said his first word, when he is well over a year old.

At this point, she will usually be reassured that he is "just a little slow." If the baby is slightly atypical in physical size also, the answer may be "He is just a little small (big) for his age. Give him time." In any case, the worried mother is assured that Johnny will "grow out of it." With this type of brain damaged child (one might almost call him the "atypical" atypical child) the diagnosis of brain damage is often not made until the characteristic learning disabilities (described in the following chapter) make themselves apparent, usually in kindergarten or the primary grades of school.

In discussing the more typical brain damaged child, we made the point that tension was a constant factor in the home, due to the difficulty in managing the routines of daily living. To a somewhat lesser extent, this is also true of the brain damaged child just described. Here there is tension also, felt by the parents who worry that their child is not developing normally. They are not really reassured by the well-meaning friends, relatives, and physicians' advice to "leave him alone and he'll be fine."

Here, each day is not a battleground as it was in Johnny's home. Rather, it becomes, especially in late infancy and early childhood, a place of waiting; waiting for that first step, for that first word, for the exciting and important landmarks of normal development. As in Johnny's home, the parent-child relationship is in jeopardy.

Until now, both types of brain damaged children discussed are those who are physically normal, at least on a gross level. These children do not appear visibly impaired, until their behavior or development or both is examined. A third type of brain damaged child also exists, however. This is the child with a motor handicap: the child with cerebral palsy. Here, in many cases, the physician, and soon the parents, are aware almost from birth of the nature of the child's handicap. Muscular rigidity, spasms, tremors, involuntary movements, abnormal muscle tone, and other physical signs can be seen by the physician and by the parents also.

Therefore, in some ways, the management of the child with cerebral palsy is easier on the parents, for at least they know what they are up against. They don't merely have a child with a "behavior problem" or one who is "just a little slow." Somehow, a visible defect makes it easier for friends, neighbors, relatives, and even the parents themselves to understand that the child really has a handicap. He isn't just willful, spoiled, or slow, as the nonphysically handicapped, brain damaged child is often characterized.

However, with cerebral palsy, too, the healthy emotional atmosphere of the home is threatened. The purely physical problems of handling a severely disabled child are many. The constant lifting and carrying of a heavy, rigid child; the often severe feeding difficulties; the problems of dressing and toileting a child with severe muscle spasms or involuntary tremors; all these place a great physical and emotional strain on the parents. Here again, warmth and affectionate interplay may suffer, often for sheer lack of parental time and energy.

So, again and again, we come to the same implicit question. What does brain damage, with or without an associated physical handicap, do to the emotional relationship between the child and his family?

The Emotional Content of the Home

There are no unusual emotional needs or symptoms of a brain damaged child. All children have certain emotional needs, and the brain damaged child is first and foremost a *child*. True, he is a child with special problems associated with his handicap, but he is, and must be recognized as, a child.

As infants, all children need love and care from their mother. They must be fed, changed, clothed, and protected from danger. As they grow, they need to learn about the world in which they live. They need experiences such as going to the store, playing in the park or playground, going for a ride in the car, seeing animals on a farm or zoo, and all the other experiences that make up a young child's world. In short, they need to see the world outside of their familiar and safe home.

As they grow still older, they must learn how to relate to other children and to the members of the family. They must learn how not to think of "me first" at all times but to be aware of the needs and desires of those around them. As adolescents and young adults, they must learn how to live in such a way that their own needs for success and security are met, along with the needs of society.

This, then, is the normal course of personality development. Many things along the line can occur which adversely affect the course described. When a mother and child do not have a normal relationship, regardless of the reason, the personality of the child will suffer. This is true regardless of whether the child is brain damaged or the mother is neglectful and abusive. Lack of social experiences and a restricted world will obstruct personality development. Here again, this lack can happen to the child limited by his severe motor handicap or to the culturally deprived child who has no one to talk to him, read to him, and take him for walks and rides. What we are saying here is, in effect, that the personality development and emotional maturity of any child, regardless of handicap, depends upon how well his life experiences have met his needs for social and emotional growth.

The only "special" emotional problems of brain damage stem from the fact that in some cases, the brain damage imposes limits upon normal social experiences and contacts with the world. Some of these limits may be caused by the physical limitations of the child which cut him off from his world. Others stem from the reactions of the parents to him, his reactions to their reactions, and so on.

It follows here that how parents react to their handicapped child, especially in infancy and early childhood, will greatly affect his future adjustment. What can parents do to give their handicapped child a good start toward a healthy emotional life?

First, the child must not be overprotected. No mother wants to let her child get into a situation where he may be physically hurt. This is true whether or not the child has a handicap. However, there are two ways of facing this problem. One is to keep the child away from all potentially dangerous situations. The better way is to take the child out into the world, show him what danger there may be, and try to teach him how to avoid the dangers. The cerebral palsied child with poor balance, who is constantly falling, isn't going to learn to adjust to this difficulty if he is kept from walking by himself. Being in a playpen or being constantly held by the hand will not teach him how to adapt to his poor balance. When he is mobile, either by crawling or walking, he should be provided with something which will protect his head, such as a football-type helmet. Then, he must be allowed to roam the house and yard as he wants. Certainly he will fall more often than the normal toddler, but the normal toddler falls often also. Indeed, the very name "toddler" describes the lack of surefootedness of this beginning explorer. The important thing is the exploration, for both the normal child and his brain damaged brother. Normal safety precautions are taken, naturally. He is not allowed to play in the street. However, the more active experiences the brain damaged child has, the more he will learn to adjust to his difficulties and learn his relationship to the world. The general rule should be that the handicapped child should be exposed to, or allowed to partake of, any type of experience that the normal child has, so long as he understands what is going on.

Along with the part experience plays in personality development, the child must have discipline and must learn to obey rules. Any child that lives within the structure of a family must learn to obey rules, share, and cooperate. This is true regardless of whether he is brain damaged or normal. Discipline shows a child that he belongs to the group, that his behavior matters to others, that his parents care about him and what he does. As long as the child can comprehend the rules of the household, he should be punished for infringing upon them. Similarly, he should be expected to share in any household duties of which he is physically capable. Barring extreme physical disability, there is no reason why the handicapped child should not clean his room, dry dishes, take out the trash, and so forth.

The child's mental abilities will affect the possibilities of emotional difficulties as he matures. For the very retarded child, the experiences outlined above, along with expressions of love and affection from his parents, will often be enough for him to achieve as much emotional and social maturity as he can. However, the needs of the brain damaged child with normal or superior intelligence are much more complex. As such a child matures, the realities of his handicap begin to affect all aspects of his life. Children want to conform and be "like the other kids." When the bright and aware brain damaged child realizes that he is different, that he is teased because he "talks funny," or that he is left out of games because he can't compete, real pressures begin. At this point, he wonders just what he is worth as a person. He questions why he is the way he is.

This is a truly difficult problem for parents to face with a loved child. Much of what they can do here depends upon what has already been done. If the child has already learned to cope with his physical or perceptual limitations, he will be better able to cope with these social pressures. If, because of discipline and participation in family life, he feels a part of a family and accepted as a full member of his family, he will have a buttress of security between him and this new hurt. But these assets are not a solution. The realities of his difference must, at some point, be faced squarely. This is a complex problem. One aspect of the complexity stems from the changing reactions of the other children. The moderately handicapped child of three or four is GENERALLY accepted by the other children in his play group. There may be some awareness of his difficulties, but it rarely causes hostility. He is accepted and allowed to play in whatever manner he can. However, when he reaches age five or six, things change. At this age, children are extremely aware of differences, which become open invitations for jeers, mimicry, and even exclusion. Thus, suddenly, the formerly accepted child finds himself "left out," by the very children who were his friends. He is bound to ask himself and his parents "Why?"

It will help if he has been exposed to other handicapped children earlier in his life, such as in a preschool group. Thus he does not suddenly become aware of his difference but comes to grips with it gradually. But this only helps; it doesn't solve the problem. When the child questions "Why?", the parents must stress all the good things in his life. He must be reassured that he is loved and that his family is proud of him. He can be taught that those who tease him are the "different" ones, because they are ill-mannered and have no understanding. But an objective handling of "WHY?" is still necessary. An explanation to the child that "God is testing you and has special faith in you" may give the child temporary solace. However, eventually the child will question why God chose HIM and what he did to deserve the doubtful distinction.

What is needed here is what is hardest to give – a clear, objective, "hard-nosed" stating of simple fact. The child is capable of understanding that there are many different kinds of people in the world; people of all shapes, sizes, and colors, people with varying degrees of abilities in many fields. Among all these different kinds of people are those who are like him. No one can explain why this is so, but it is. There are many differences between people, and it is up to each person to take stock of himself and use his abilities to the utmost. When the child is older and capable of benefitting from the experience, contact with handicapped people who have "made it" may help him to see that he, too, can live a useful life.

The handicap cannot be and should not be denied. It is there and it is going to be there always. But the child should be helped to believe that with help from teachers, doctors, therapists, and other professionals, and with hard work on his part, he can truly make the best of his life. It is up to him to try and keep trying. He must learn that if he fails, he must pick himself up, mentally and physically, and try again, until he succeeds. This is not only his role but that of everyone in life. It may be a little harder for the brain damaged child to do it, but he can if he has the will.

This attitude isn't instilled overnight. The child must know that his parents think he can make each hurdle, but he must not feel that if, at any one time he fails, his parents will love him less. He needs to be encouraged to try, praised on succeeding, and accepted and further encouraged upon failing. In short, the child must accept the limits put on him by his handicap and yet be constantly willing to push himself to these limits, to do every last thing that he can. He must feel that there is always a goal to be reached, even if success isn't always immediately forthcoming.

Here we have talked a great deal about the child's feeling of his value, but we must not lose sight of the fact that there is more than just his own value to consider. He must also learn to appreciate the value of others and to consider their needs and feelings. He must not step on others in his rush up his own personal Jacob's ladder. The child needs to learn that he has a responsibility to others and he should learn this early in life. He needs experience in sharing and in occasionally letting others have what they want, even if his desires aren't fulfilled. He must never have the control of family activities, social experiences, et cetera. He should not be allowed to ALWAYS choose the program on television. His normal brothers and sisters have rights also. Sometimes we are so busy showing the handicapped child that he is "somebody" that it is hard to remember that the somebody is a PART of a family and not the ruling member.

Without this training, all the professional help, all the desire to succeed, all the self-acceptance in the world, and all the encouragement from his parents will avail the child nothing. He will become a willful, selfish, demanding person who will then be truly handicapped, not by his physical disability but by his crippled personality.

CHAPTER TWO

DIAGNOSIS OF
THE BRAIN DAMAGED CHILD

W E have already discussed what it sometimes is like to live with a brain damaged child and what problems can be caused in parent-child relationships. Many of these problems can and do occur long before the child is diagnosed as brain damaged, except in the case of an early detectable problem such as cerebral palsy. Accepting that their child is "different" is perhaps the most difficult realization parents ever have to make. Depending upon the visibility of the problem, this realization may come abruptly or dawn very gradually. But when it hits, the parents' second reaction (the first often is an understandable and, hopefully, temporary grieving) is to want to find out who can tell them what is wrong with Johnny and who can cure him. Often their first visit is to their own physician. As we have discussed earlier, in many cases this proves to be unsatisfactory. Brain damage is still a relatively little understood childhood problem. Many good family doctors have had no experience with it and little, if any, contact with it in medical literature. Much well-meaning but useless advice can be given to the parents by a professional person unaware of the complexities and varying aspects of childhood brain damage. Often the parents are told to wait until the child outgrows his problem. But he doesn't outgrow it. Sometimes they are advised that he is emotionally disturbed, because of his erratic and unstable behavior. This can be disastrous to the parents' shaky security and can add to their burden of guilt and doubt. With all the watered-down child psychology theories put forth in the popular magazines of today, every mother "knows" that the only reason for emotional disturbance in her child is because she has done something wrong. In actuality, this need not be true. But in any case, Johnny's mother needn't worry about what she did or didn't do, since Johnny is not emotionally disturbed but brain damaged. Obviously, being told that he is "disturbed" will not alleviate the strain already felt in the household, due to the child's behavioral problems.

If the parents happen to have a physician who has had contact with childhood brain damage, they will fare better. In this case, the diagnosis may be made early enough for the child to be able to benefit from specialized training at the preschool level.

It is often a pediatrician, rather than a general practitioner, who is more likely to recognize childhood brain damage. The reason for this is fairly obvious. The general practitioner sees patients of all ages, from infancy through old age. He may never see enough children in any one age group to formulate a thumbnail picture of the normal child at that age. The pediatrician, on the other hand, sees only children. His practice is limited to children. He, therefore, has a great deal of experience with children of all ages. He develops a "seat of the pants" feel for those whose behavior or development or both doesn't fall within the norms. Such a doctor's feel should not be ignored.

Very often, when brain damage is suspected, the parents are referred by their doctor to a pediatric neurologist. He is a specialist in the problems of the brain and nervous system, common to childhood. He will look for what are known as "hard" signs of brain damage, which may or may not be apparent, even though the child is brain damaged. He checks for abnormal or absent reflexes, for difficulties in eye focus, for abnormal movements of the eyes, for atypical sounds made when the skull is tapped, for varying degrees of strength on one side of the body as compared to the other side, and many other "hard" clinical signs. He will usually supervise the administering of an electroencephalogram to determine if the child's brain wave pattern is abnormal. More often than not, unless the child has epileptic seizures of some sort, associated with his brain damage, there will not be any abnormality of the brain waves. There may not be any of the above mentioned signs.

From this, we can see that a pediatric neurologist can confirm a tentative diagnosis of brain damage, if he finds positive symptoms. However, lack of these symptoms does not rule out the presence of brain damage. For along with "hard" signs, there are "soft" signs, which are usually discovered by the third member of the team involved in diagnosis of childhood brain damage, the clinical psychologist.

It is the role of the clinical psychologist to evaluate these "soft" signs. Very often, the recognizable symptoms of childhood brain damage are seen more clearly in the psychological testing situation, than at any other time. This is particularly true of the child who is not a marked behavior problem in the home.

The function of the clinical psychologist is to choose, administer, and evaluate the proper intellectual, perceptual, verbal, and performance tests. If many of the various symptoms of childhood brain damage become apparent upon evaluation of a child's performance on these tests, a diagnosis of brain damage can be made by the clinical psychologist. In the next chapter, these symptoms will be gone into in great detail. At this point, it suffices to identify them in the context of psychological testing.

We often think of the clinical psychologist as administering only "intelligence tests." It is true that these are an important part of his test battery and that a certain type of performance on intelligence quotient tests can indicate brain damage. When looking for signs of brain damage, it is not the relative level of the IQ that is the determinant. There are brain damaged children with IQs far above average, and there are those with marked intellectual deficits. There are also cases falling anywhere between these two extremes. What concerns the psychologist here is the concept of "psychometric scatter." This can be understood if we realize that most children are fairly even in their abilities. One may be better in reading than in arithmetic. Another may be better at arithmetic than spelling. But, roughly speaking, a child with a mental age of six years will fall between five and one half years, and six and one half years, on all of the various abilities tested by intelligence tests. There will not be a scattering of scores from three years to ten years, for example. This is not case with the brain damaged child. In fact, the comparison between the levels of performance on various subtests within an IQ test can give an excellent picture of the problems associated with brain damage that the child has. Such difficulties as poor abstract reasoning, poor vocabulary, or problems in memory can quickly demonstrate themselves when the child is given a valid intellectual test.

However, as stated before, although we often think of IQ tests as the sole activity of clinical psychology, these tests are not the be all and end all of the repetoire. Other materials that help to demonstrate some of the signs of brain damage are perceptual-motor tests, such as formboards and puzzles; tests of ability to copy forms and draw forms from memory; and tests of abstracting abilities, such as similarities between objects. When such tests demonstrate perceptual-motor problems, difficulties in shifting from one type of response to another, difficulties in abstract language, and so forth, the psychologist sees further indicators of childhood brain damage.

Other important pieces of information are gained during the testing situation. The psychologist can see the child's method of dealing with a test and whether or not the child appears to relate to him. Signs of great emotional stress during testing, often indicators of previously experienced failure, tell the psychologist a great deal. Aspects of the child's language are important here, such as whether his conversation makes sense or whether it jumps from one thought to another without any logical sequence. The child's level of language comprehension can also be seen. The psychologist looks for the general behavioral signs of brain damage, such as problems in attention, difficulties in sitting still, and tendencies to laugh or cry too easily.

In the final analysis, since so many cases of childhood brain damage lack observable "hard" medical signs identifiable to the neurologist, it is the perceptual, behavioral, and intellectual deviances brought to light by the clinical psychologist that often lead to the definite diagnosis of childhood brain damage.

In any case, the diagnosis is finally made, hopefully at an early age, but all too often not until the child has tried and failed in a normal classroom. At this point, the parents want to know what brain damage means and what can be done to help their child. They must have a clear understanding of the learning problems and problems of social interaction that make up the behavioral signs of childhood brain damage. They need to be told what they can do to minimize the difficulties at home that are caused by the child's handicap. The following chapters are an attempt to deal with these complex subjects.

CHAPTER THREE

SPECIAL PROBLEMS
OF CHILDHOOD BRAIN DAMAGE
Educational and Social Implications

Attention Defects

CHILDREN who are brain damaged have many different attention disturbances. These fall into three main types, called by the psychologists hyperirritability of attention, general hyperactivity, and drifting attention.

Hyperirritability of attention refers to the difficulty in selecting one thing to which to attend out of a whole field of possible choices. This is a basic difficulty in distinguishing between the important object, or figure, to perceive and its background of unrelated and momentarily unimportant objects. Children with this difficulty are often referred to as being distractable. They find it difficult to limit themselves to what they should be seeing, hearing, doing, or learning. They live in a chaotic world where no one thing is more important than another, in terms of attention. Thus, the sound of their mother's voice is no more demanding of attention than the sound of water running in the sink, a sound a normal child would ignore in favor of the voice.

This problem can be dealt with. At first, the child needs to have a very limited world. Things which he is not to see or hear should be removed from his field of attention. Classrooms should be plain and uncluttered. Extraneous sounds should be cut to a minimum. However, this is only a first step. The child needs an opportunity to learn how to select out the things to which he must attend. He will not always live in a world where only the important things are in view but in a world where the important things are imbedded in a stimulating background of extraneous sights, smells, and sounds. The increase in stimulating background objects must be done

17

gradually, to build up the child's ability to deal with the necessary choices in attention.

An important tool here is the child's desire to attend. If he is kept busy and interested in what he is doing, his own interest in his task will screen out the potentially distracting background.

Another attention problem is known as general hyperactivity. It must be clearly understood at the outset of any discussion of hyperactivity that the child's apparently aimless wandering, fidgeting, and squirming is not purposeful misbehaving. Hyperactivity is a compulsive behavior, caused and driven by his brain damage. It is a reaction to his inability to select out a suitable focus for his attention.

Hyperactivity is controlled in much the same way as hyperirritable attention. The starting point, again, is limiting of distractions and limiting also of the physical space for movement that is available to the child. In many cases, extremely hyperactive children function better under physical restraints, such as a table surrounding the child on three sides, like a young child's feeding table.

The actual physical limiting of the child, whether in such a table, in your lap, or in a small bare room, gives him a sense of physical security, tells him where he is physically, and simplifies his choice of objects to which to attend. This reduces his hyperactivity.

However, as with training in hyperirritable attention, this restraint and restricted environment is only a first step. Again, the child's tolerance for freer situations must be expanded, while enabling him to retain his sense of where he is, physically, in relation to space. He needs to learn the physical boundaries of the place in which he is and to learn where he ends and the place begins. Much of his wandering earlier was an attempt to discover just that.

The third type of attention defect is drifting attention. This is not as common as the first two problems but occurs in some brain damaged children as well as in children with other problems.

It can be seen as a weak and brief attention span. Unlike the distractable or hyperactive child, the child doesn't lose attention to one object because of the strong pull of many other objects.

Rather, the child lacks the ability to follow through on any one activity. He may start to do a puzzle. He will pick up a piece and then hold it in his hand or drop it, while he "goes off into his own little world."

Attention disturbances have been dealt with first here because of a belief that correcting or relieving this area of difficulty is basic to the success of all educational and therapy programs for the brain damaged child. The establishing of stable attention habits is necessary, before improvement can be made in other areas.

Deviant Propositionality

Inherent in any discussion of deviant propositionality is an understanding of the concept of propositionality, itself. A "proposition" is defined as a conscious act, with a goal, that is planned, step by step. This is contrasted with a·"nonpropositional act" that is not directed toward a goal and an "act of lowered propositionality" that has, through practice and habit, become automatic and requires no step-by-step planning.

A characteristic of a proposition is that its "level of propositionality" is largely controlled by factors of the situation.

A few examples of propositions and nonpropositions may clear up any confusion here. If someone says "How are the kids?" to you as you are scurrying along downtown on your way shopping, you generally answer "fine." This reponse occurs even if the children actually have the measles. This is nonpropositional speech. However, if something in the situation, such as your feeling for the person who is asking, makes you stop and consider your answer, rather than answering automatically, you may say "The kids have the measles." This is propositional speech.

Physical acts other than speech can be propositional also. The printing of the small letter "d" is highly propositional to the six-year-old who learns to do it sequentially. He first painstakingly makes a "c." Then he adds the vertical line going from the bottom of the "c" up to the next line. The adult prints a "d" with no conscious thought to the way in which it is to be done. For him, the act of printing a "d" is nonpropositional.

Another aspect of propositionality relates to the context in which the act is performed. Many acts which are nonpropositional in some contexts are highly propositional in others. Going back to our example of printing "d," if the adult in question was suddenly asked to pinch-hit for the teacher in a first grade class and teach the children how to print a "d," he would find himself thinking of each step involved as he printed the letter. The act of printing "d" would become propositional.

The implications of propositionality for brain damaged children are fairly clear. Due to motor problems, attention problems and perceptual problems, as well as to a history of social problems and failures, complex behaviors do not become automatic as quickly for the brain damaged child as the normal child. Propositional effects on behavior happen to everyone. Deviant propositionality refers to a gross exaggeration of these effects on the brain damaged child.

We see this demonstrated easily with brain damaged children every day. A parent learns from a teacher or therapist that Johnny can write his name or sing a song. Delighted, the parent says "Johnny, write your name for mommy." But the fact of mommy asking for the act, rather than the therapist or teacher for whom he has done it countless times, changes the level of propositionality. Johnny fails.

There is no quick cure for deviant propositionality. For short-term, fairly simple tasks, such as writing "d," constant practice, way beyond the point of initial success, seems to be an effective way of making sure that the child can succeed even under pressure. However, a general lowering of propositionality (or conversely, a generalized ability to tolerate higher propositionality) is a long-term process. Indeed it appears that deviant propositionality is one of the most tenacious of the "soft" signs of brain damage. It may be reduced as the child's generalized difficulties are reduced. The level of propositional tolerance may be markedly raised. But in the long run, for any given class of behaviors, such as speech, physical activities, and so forth, the likelihood of difficulty, due to the pressures of the situation (the level of propositionality), remains present to some extent throughout the life of the brain damaged person.

Catastrophic Behavior

Catastrophic behavior can be defined as a number of nonadaptive (not useful) reactions to stress. In discussing these reactions we must return to our discussion of deviant propositionality. We have defined the level of propositionality in terms of the level of conscious thinking required to organize an act. Nonpropositional behaviors, which are relatively automatic, require little conscious thought. As propositionality increases, consciousness is involved more and more in the performing of the act. This leads to a vicious circle where the brain damaged is concerned. Because of his difficulties, as discussed earlier, there are few automatic acts open to him. Therefore, he must function at high propositional levels most of the time. This stress forces him to be continually alert and ready, always highly conscious of all of his behavior. For example, the child with difficulties in perceiving differences in depth cannot automatically walk up or down the stairs. Since most of daily functioning involves some aspect of performance that is deviant in the brain damaged child, he is under the tension of constant propositionality. Thus, every new demand for action, every change in a situation adds further stress and becomes a threat to his security.

We have already stated that with increased propositionality, activities the child can perform in other situations are failed. Catastrophic behavior occurs when the demands of his life raise the propositionality of some act for the child to a degree where he can no longer react usefully to the demand. He fails and he cannot reorganize himself to begin over appropriately.

We now understand why a catastrophic reaction is triggered, but we have yet to discuss what constitutes a catastrophic reaction. One component, and one most commonly associated with childhood brain damage, is emotional lability and reactive inappropriateness. Emotional lability refers to the extreme ease with which brain damaged children cry, laugh, and have temper tantrums. The labile child is the child who cries at a slight reprimand, who gets the giggles over something only moderately amusing, and who may hit, kick, or bite a sister or brother who accidentally bumped into him.

Crying, laughing, and fighting all are kinds of reactive behavior; that is, they are reactions to something. Reactive inappropriateness refers to the fact that these behaviors are inappropriate in terms of the means of expression and the length and strength of the outburst.

These disturbances aren't always related to propositional stress, but such stress intensifies the reactions to a marked extent. Therefore, at low levels of propositionality, the behaviors described above, such as the giggles or crying, may occur. The means of expression may be inappropriate. For example, the child may laugh when he is scolded or cry when he is praised. Catastrophic reactions involving emotional lability and reactive inappropriateness occur when the child is faced with too high a propositional level. The reaction takes many forms: screaming, crying uncontrollably, throwing things, kicking the mother, and so on. This reaction is a sign that the child is being pushed too far and asked to perform some act that is propositionally beyond him. The total situation he is in, such as a houseful of strangers all talking to him and expecting him to answer, may be of too great a propositional level. At this point, all that can be done is to remove the child from the situation, usually physically. A better method by far is to be able to recognize, before it happens, that a catastrophic reaction is about to occur and to alter the situation to avoid it.

There are a number of warning signals which can alert a parent to an impending storm. If these are learned and the propositionality somehow decreased, the storm can be averted. One such sign is known as vasomotor lability. It is seen as sudden perspiration, flushing, pallor, and change in breathing and pulse rate. In some brain damaged children, these signs occur regularly, without stress, and are therefore "normal" for these children. But in the brain damaged child who does not normally show vasomotor lability, this is an early warning signal, to be heeded or else.

Another signal is perseveration. Again, perseveration has many implications, many of which relate to other factors than catastrophic reaction. We will here consider only the relationship between perseveration and catastrophic reaction. Perseveration refers to the child's tendency to repeat any given simple response, when it is no longer appropriate to the demands of the situation. For example, the child can print both "c's" and "d's" and is asked to produce a row of alternate "c" and "d." Instead, he prints "c," "d," "d," "d," "d." He can tell the difference between the two. He can produce both of them. He understands that he is to make first one and then the other, and so on. The fact is that he has difficulty in changing from one response to another. This is perseverated response. As we have just said, it can occur for many reasons. If it occurs along with either increased emotional lability or vasomotor lability, or both, it can be taken as a sign of impending catastrophic reaction.

All this gives us an indication that the child cannot cope with the level of propositionality. The situation must be restructured so that he can cope with it. We have already discussed ways of improving attention and reducing hyperactivity. Now we must find out what contributes to situational propositionality and how to deal with it. This brings us to a consideration of linguistic and intellective function. The difficulties involved in these functions can lead to severe situational stress for the brain damaged child.

Linguistic and General Intellective Functions

Among the characteristic problems in this area common to brain damaged children, one of the most important is deviant abstracting and categorizing processes. This problem is very common and very limiting. Usually, the child's language is extremely concrete and very rigid in concept formation. The child's concepts of "same" and "different" are limited because he cannot deal with more than one concept at a time. For example, a big ball and a small ball are not seen as both being alike, but as two separate and distinct objects. The concept that both are balls, although they differ in size, does not come naturally to the brain damaged child but must be taught. This inability to generalize is a major problem. Generalized categorizing concepts develop very slowly in the brain damaged child and often develop only through specialized teaching.

This tends to isolate the brain damaged child from his world. It makes the world a very chaotic place, as each thing in the world is a separate entity, not a part of a classifiable, and thus understandable, category.

Along with concreteness and difficulty in generalization, there is also a tendency for abnormal abstraction and generalization. Usually this is due to the fact that the child has difficulty in selecting the most defining characteristic on which to classify objects and situations. This is different from the simple abstractions of a very young child. It is a bizarre linguistic difficulty. The young child will tell you that cows and horses are alike because they both have four legs. It takes a good deal of sophistication, linguistically, to come to the concept of "animals," as defining the alikeness of cows and horses. But if a child says that cows and horses are alike "because they don't live in our house" or "because they aren't people," this is a problem of deviant abstraction and generalization.

Deviant abstraction and categorization is not limited only to verbalized classification and relatively complex abstractions. In some cases, it can be seen at simple levels as well. This problem can be typified by the difficulty in matching objects on the basis of form or color, two low-level abstracting tasks.

Along with complete failure in categorization and abstraction, demonstrated by an inability to produce any response when asked, for example, to group objects by form or color, there are other reactions which show difficulty in abstraction or categorization or both. One such difficulty is an inability to maintain what is known as "set" for a particular task. For example, if given objects consisting of circles, triangles, and squares in different colors and being asked to group them so they "go together," the child may begin by sorting on the basis of color and then shift to form sorting before he finishes color sorting. Thus, he has lost his "set" for color.

The opposite reaction may also occur. There can be an inability to shift from one sorting basis to another. Thus, when the child has correctly sorted the objects for either color or form and is asked "Can you group them any other way?" he becomes disorganized and cannot make the shift. This is what is meant by being rigid in terms of concept formation. Indeed, this difficulty is known as "conceptual rigidity."

Conceptual rigidity differs from perseveration, previously discussed under catastrophic reaction, although the difference is a fine one. Perseveration is usually a reaction to propositionality. It is defined as being a repetition of a previous response, a single "unit" of behavior. For example, the child identifies a picture of a cow with the word "cow" and then proceeds to identify the remaining pictures in the series with the word "cow," although they are not pictures of a cow. This is a repetition of a single response, the word "cow." Conceptual rigidity refers to difficulty or inability in shifting from one basis for categorization or abstracting to another basis, such as from color to form.

Another difficulty with abstraction seen in brain damaged children is that of categorizations and abstractions that are "correct" but made on the basis of factors not considered prime factors for abstraction. Let us return to the example of the child who says that cows and horses are alike because "they aren't people." This is correct; cows and horses AREN'T people. However, the factor of being "not people" is not the quality which determines the similarity of cows and horses.

Such difficulties are not caused by senseless or incorrect selections of abstracting factors; rather, they are selections based upon qualities not ordinarily seen as being prime selection qualities.

We have seen that abstracting and generalizing problems vary in form. They also vary in intensity. At some levels, there may be no such function at all. At higher levels, we find children who can perform simple abstractions (such as grouping by form or color) but who fail at more complex abstractions, such as sorting for colors when many shades of colors are included.

Another difficulty we have discussed is one where the child makes selections but on the basis of factors not generally used as a basis for categorization. There are also problems where the child begins to categorize normally but cannot continue to generalize the categorization when the choices are more complex.

It can be seen that these abstracting and categorizing difficulties are obstacles to normal methods of acquiring information. These problems represent a severe learning problem in terms of normal educational methods. Procedures for relieving such difficulties are long and complicated and require specialized techniques of teaching linguistic concepts, based on a general analysis of the child's linguistic functions. What is needed here is for the teacher to know whether the child has basic linguistic concepts around which are built the abstracting and categorizing functions. Does he understand the relationship between "more and less" or "greater and fewer"? Does he have a concept of numbers as indicators of definite quantities or are they just numerals learned by memory? Does he have concepts enabling him to compare objects, such as "same," "different," "bigger," and "smaller"? These and many other concepts are the building blocks from which the towers of abstraction and categorization are built.

This "language development" approach to relieving abstracting and categorizing difficulties is geared toward giving the child these linguistic tools. The child must be helped to interpret the world linguistically.

As already stated, the first step is to determine the general level of linguistic function. If the child is at a very low level linguistically, he will need to start with identification of objects. When the child is identifying objects, generalization is introduced. The child is asked to pick out all the horses or all the cows, regardless of color, size, posture, and so forth. As he picks out each one, his teacher qualifies them by saying "that's a BLACK horse," "that's a BIG horse," and so on.

When a large number of nouns have been generalized in this way, conceptual generalization is begun. Now all horses and cows are grouped together and the child is asked to "give me all the black animals" or "give me all the big animals." This introduces the notion that descriptive terms may serve as categories (big, small) and that objects with specific names (horse, cow) can be classified under a generalized term (animals). This is a huge step and a difficult one for brain damaged children.

Classifying concepts are introduced here: horses, dogs, and cows are animals; hats, shoes, and dresses are clothing. Eventually the child will begin to categorize other groups himself, once he is taught to categorize some groups. He need not be taught "everything" but only enough different concepts so that he understands the process.

He should go at this point from objects to pictures and eventually from pictures to words alone. Words must become meaningful symbols through which he comprehends and alters his world.

At this high level, we are concerned with not only the child's ability to group things but with his ability to understand and deal with his world on a verbal level. Here we deal with questions such as "In what way is a cat like a dog?" The child must be taught to think about the function of things, rather than just their size, shape, color, et cetera. (Trains and buses are similar because they both are means of transportation.) Some brain damaged children show no linguistic difficulty until this level of abstraction is reached.

Up to this point, we have been discussing one class of difficulties with linguistic and intellective functions. The next to be discussed is difficulty in grammar and syntax. Many children with brain damage have difficulty in the use of abstract words or words for which there are little concrete references. Thus, prepositions and some adverbs and other modifiers are omitted in sentence formation. This is known as "agrammatic" or "telegraphic" speech. Along with this is usually seen a confusion in pronoun use. This is an important problem, because it leads to difficulty on the part of the listener in understanding a child's meaningful communication. The meaning becomes evident only if the listener understands the pattern of communication used by the child. For example, "Me party class" is a concrete (no abstract words) and telegraphic way of saying "I had a party in my class." Failure to understand the child's meaning can lead to severe frustration for him. The child's parents, teacher, and therapists must learn to associate the child's daily activities and his language problems and come up with an understanding of the content of his language. Children with severe difficulties in language output may have adequate language comprehension abilities. Such a child knows, from the response the listener gives to his speech, that he is not being understood. This frustrating situation often triggers a catastrophic reaction and can be dangerous to the relationship between the child and the listener, be he teacher, therapist, or parent. The listener must learn how to interpret the deviant language so that he can communicate with the child. For example, in response to "me party class," his mother could say "Was the party today" or "Will the party be tomorrow?" Such questions will lead to further responses from the child, which, although still not grammatically adequate, will help the child clarify what he wants to say. For example, if the party is to be held tomorrow, he might respond "tomorrow party."

In this way, the parent and child can communicate about what has happened at school. (The same is true for the teacher or therapist interested in what the child is telling him about his home activities.) The important thing is that the child is helped to use his limited ability to communicate to the utmost.

Another linguistic difficulty of brain damaged children is what is called an "anomic" or "amnesic" reaction. This refers to a difficulty in finding the proper word for an object. "Amnesic" actually is an oversimplified explanatory term, since it infers that the word has been forgotten. This is not the case. The word is not forgotten. The child is unable to call it from memory under ordinary conditions. This can be seen from the following example. If the child is shown a picture of a car and asked what it is, he may say "I don't know" or answer incorrectly. But if given the picture along with other pictures of other objects and asked to point to the car, he may be able to do so correctly and promptly. Thus, he hasn't forgotten the word "car," but he could not bring it forth when asked to do so. Another clue to the fact that the word is not forgotten in an "anomic" reaction is the "roundabout" technique. If the child is shown a picture of a glass, he may be unable to name it. If he is told "you drink from a _____" (with a rising inflection and the noun left blank), he will immediately respond "glass."

The final type of linguistic difficulty to be discussed here is a difficulty with serial order. This is related to the anomic difficulty discussed above, because it is a problem in calling forth information when needed. However, it is particularly related to calling forth serialized information. This is often displayed in a problem in rote counting. The difficulty is not with number concepts but with the ability to call forth the correct number word. The child can demonstrate number concepts by placing, upon command, the correct number of blocks in a box and yet be unable to count the blocks verbally.

These are only a highlighting of the linguistic and intellective difficulties associated with childhood brain damage. Any one child may have all, some, or none of these problems and may have many other difficulties in this area. There is no "typical" brain injured child!

Visual Perceptual Problems

One of the basic problems in this area, and one which received much early attention in the study of the defects associated with childhood brain damage, is what is called a "figure-ground" disturbance. The brain damaged child has difficulty in separating out the central foreground (or figure) from the background (ground) components of a visual stimulus. There are varying degrees of difficulty with figure-ground perception. There may be a smoothing out of the differences between the figure and ground, resulting in a lack of precision in seeing objects. There may be a lack of stable separation between figure and ground, so that the two may fluctuate, or even reverse (with the ground then perceived as figure). There may be complete failure in separation of the two components, leading to a mixing of central and background stimuli.

The presence of figure-ground disturbances in children who are brain damaged is well established and has been demonstrated in many experiments. However, this problem does not explain all the perceptual difficulties seen in brain damaged children. Figure-ground disturbances are only one of the visual perceptual problems associated with childhood brain damage.

Even in cases where figure-ground relationships aren't involved, discrimination of forms (or the distinction of one figure from another figure, rather than from ground) is difficult for many brain damaged children. Brain damaged children also have difficulty in seeing the relationship between a whole and its parts. For example, if a brain damaged child is given a picture of a square and a number of lines of various lengths and angles, he might have extreme difficulty in selecting the lines needed to reproduce the square. Brain damaged children show significantly poorer abilities than normal children also in ability to choose a part needed to complete an incomplete picture of a circle, square, or triangle. Thus, they have difficulty in integrating parts into a whole (the lines that make up a square) or in integrating an incompleted figure into a whole.

So far, we have treated visual perception as a simple function, involving only vision. Tests of function very often involve more than pure vision, such as a test asking a child to draw what he sees. Studies have shown that visual perceptual development involves integrating information from many senses. But brain damaged children can't always integrate. For example, many brain damaged children can match and identify forms (purely vision) but, although they are not paralyzed, may not be able to reproduce the form by drawing it. A brain damaged child asked to reproduce a given design may fail the task but be able to tell the difference between his production and the model. He may even show awareness of the incorrect details of his production and yet be unable to match the test pattern. Obviously, a test of visual perception requiring only reproduction of test pictures or patterns can give misleading information about the child's ability to match or discriminate the pictures or patterns. We must remember that some children can match and discriminate but cannot reproduce, as we have just seen.

It follows, therefore, that when evaluating visual perception, two aspects should be tested; pure recognition and discrimination, and reproduction (a perceptual-motor ability, rather than a "purely perceptual" one). We must be able to make distinctions between failures or distortions in discriminative ability and failures at a perceptual-motor level. Failures in discrimination are at a much lower level and must have basic training in such things as form recognition. Perceptual-motor difficulty without discriminative difficulties are at a higher level and require different methods of training.

Perceptual-motor difficulty is much more subtle than a primary visual perceptual difficulty, such as form discrimination. Basic perceptual functions are not impaired, but the perceptions cannot be transformed into a motor activity. This is known as "apraxia." Apraxia, although labeled a perceptual-motor problem, is not related to paralysis (actually, an apraxic child can be paralyzed as well, but these are two separate disabilities). Apraxia occurs when the child has the motor capability to perform a given physical act but cannot plan the act (motor planning) or change a visual perception into a motor reaction. As stated earlier, this can be distinguished from a simple perceptual difficulty, depending upon whether or not the child can match, identify, or recognize visual stimuli. If he can, and in the absence of demonstrable paralysis, he is still unable to reproduce a drawing or fit together the pieces of a puzzle (although he indicates he knows where they go), this is apraxia.

The example of the puzzle may appear confusing without further explanation. We may wonder how a child can demonstrate that he knows where the parts go and yet not be able to fit the pieces in. Let us imagine a puzzle consisting of basic geometric forms to be fitted into correspondingly shaped recesses in a puzzle tray. The child may quite easily fit in the circle form, which requires no turning of the piece in order to fit it into the circle-shaped recess. Suppose, however, that he next picks up the star. In order to fit it in the star-shaped recess, he must then turn the piece about, until the points match the points on the recess. He may pick the piece up and bring it directly to the star recess (demonstrating that he knows where the piece goes). At this point, if he is apraxic, he will fumble about, not knowing *how* to turn the piece so that it will fit.

Apraxia, in itself, is a severe problem. But an apraxia in the early life of a child can deteriorate into an even more serious primary perceptual problem in later development. There are two basic reasons for this possible deterioration. One lies in the basic learning process. Any learning, including perceptual learning, is dependent in part upon reinforcement (or reward for success).

Let us return to the star in the puzzle. The child sees the star, picks it up, locates the proper hole and finds out that for some reason beyond his comprehension, the star doesn't fit into the hole that looks like a star. He is not rewarded for his correct perception. This happens in many situations. He starts out to copy a drawing of a square and ends up making a circle. He turns his bike so as to get through the doorway and bumps into the wall. As we can see, the apractic child has to live in a world where he may see things exactly as other children do but where seeing doesn't give him any information about reacting. He learns that how the world looks to him doesn't tell him how to react appropriately to it. He learns that what he sees may not help him make an appropriate motor response.

Gradually, while nonapractic children are developing higher levels of complex visual discrimination, the apractic child, because of a lack of stability between how the world looks and what happens when he responds to it, does not develop higher levels of discrimination. He fails to increase his attention to perceptual detail (what value does increased attention hold for him?). Eventually, he may be far behind the nonapractic child in developing higher level visual perceptual skills.

The above explains the development of primary perceptual difficulty from apraxia on the basis of learning. Apraxia can be equally detrimental to the development of perceptual skills in terms of neurological organization. Perceptual skills, particularly higher level skills such as complex discrimination or spatial perception, are highly dependent upon association between visual stimuli and the feedback established by the motor responses to the visual world. Apraxia can be viewed as leading to unstable or distorted feedback, false information about the results of one's body movements. Thus, disruption of visual perception can be a natural end product of apractic difficulties.

With the child who is motor handicapped, perceptual disturbances can be on the same basis as for the apractic. Again, one of the key factors in perceptual development is the interaction of motor response and visual stimulus. With the severely cerebral palsied child, who cannot walk and who has little hand function, the opportunity for this interaction is limited. This is also true for the less handicapped child who can walk but whose motor responses are erratic and variable. Visual perception depends in part upon constancies of visual-motor interaction. A limiting of such relationships may retard perceptual development.

In the normal child, these interrelationships between visual stimulus and motor response feedback occur automatically. At first, activities are gross and inaccurate, such as the baby's attempt to reach a moving object. Gradually, with maturation, accuracy increases and a stable pattern of visual motor interactions develops. These enable the child to judge size, shape, distance, and so forth. They also enable him to determine his own relationship to his surroundings. This happens in such a way that SEEING becomes the automatic guide for DOING.

However, for the child with erratic or absent motor abilities, there is little opportunity for such development. He finds that seeing DOESN'T always lead to doing. He reaches for a glass and knocks it over. He steps toward the door and bumps into the door-jamb. Sometimes, certainly, he succeeds, but success is not dependable. It is not constant. Thus, spatial concepts develop slowly, fine discrimination remains undeveloped; and thus, severe motor disabilities can retard perceptual development.

All this would indicate that training in visual perception for brain damaged children should be aimed at establishing stable interactions between visual stimuli and motor responses. It must clarify and stabilize the child's visual-motor interactions. Training should not be only in discrimination and identification. The total child must be involved in visual perceptual training. The brain damaged child must be taught to "see and do," just as the normal child learns this automatically. He must have as much active motor experience as possible. He needs activities which allow for the visual-motor experiences inherent to the development of perception in the normal child. He must establish stable relationships between his body and the surroundings he sees. He must learn that certain constant relationships exist between what he sees and what his body does.

At the lowest level, this involves simple visual attention to objects that move. The child will randomly look and reach for the object, particularly if it makes a noise, such as a rattle or a bell. Eventually, for the normal child, random reaching will cease and the child learns to reach for the object and then strike it to make a sound. The brain damaged child must be helped to do this. After experience with random activity and striking of the rattle or bell, the bell must be moved in such a way that the child can strike it only when he looks at it. In other words, the pleasurable reward of the movement occurs only when the object is in the child's sight. Sometimes, particularly for the motor handicapped child, the object will need to be pushed into contact with the child's hand whenever he looks at it. The goal is to establish a stable perceptual-motor pattern of "looking and reaching."

With the older child in need of such training, the reinforcing object might not be bells but a piece of candy, which he must look at and reach for. The goal is the same: looking and reaching leads to a reward; there is no reward for reaching without looking.

After looking and reaching, perceptual-motor development becomes quite complex and many different facets of development occur at once. Certain elements must occur before others, but one is not always completed before another begins. The order in which development is presented in the next paragraphs merely indicates which facets begin before others, but it must be borne in mind that many facets are in different stages of completion at the same time.

Looking and reaching leads to awareness of spatial relationships in terms of the child's own movements. His awareness of the relationship between what he sees, what he does, and its effects on him depend on his motor interactions with his world. The normal child develops this as his mobility increases from crawling, to walking, to climbing, and so on. Along with this comes sharpening of form perception. Visual perception is blended with information from his other senses and a total perceptual system develops. The information from one sense adds to and clarifies information from other senses. It also allows for a system of cross-checks to help clarify situations that are ambiguous in terms of a single sense perception. For example, a lump of uncast glass and a lump of ice may look very similar to a person who has had no physical contact with either. After touching each one and becoming aware of the differences in touch, the person usually can distinguish the visual differences, however small, quite clearly.

For the brain damaged child, visual attention is a first step in the child's learning the relationships between himself and the world he sees. Structured visual-motor experience must be greatly expanded, and the child must have active structured experience in exploration of his world. This enables the child to establish a stable "world-self" relationship. It also ensures that visual stimuli will be important in calling forth and guiding motor responses. Both hand activities and activities requiring moving around a room are necessary for this development. The concern is not to teach the child to crawl or walk, or to use his hands, but to enable him to learn that he can depend upon what he sees. He must learn, for example, that he can move across a horizontal surface and will bump into a vertical one and that the two have different, and consistent, visual aspects.

Obviously, these experiences are difficult to obtain for the cerebral palsied, nonmobile child. Regardless of the difficulty, it is essential that such experienes occur and as early in life as possible. Even if the child is placed on a floor where he can roll or crawl about, in whatever manner he can, this movement in a visual world is vitally important. Whatever bumps and bruises he might obtain are far less important than the value of the visual-motor experience. As early as possible, visual control of direction of body movement and of hand movement should be taught in play activities. Activities such as the "run and fetch" games that young children enjoy are good activities here. As the object is placed in a corner, along a wall, or in the center of a room, the child learns to deal on a visual-motor level with these spatial relationships, as he fetches the toy.

It is important to note here that motor activity OF ITSELF does not create perception. Motor experience helps to supplement and clarify visual experience, but only when the motor act occurs along with a perceptual act. Perception is made clearer by physical action but is not created by it.

We have seen how moving about and using his hands can give meaning to what the child sees. Through moving in the world the child learns the relationship between himself and the world. Through touch, he learns to more easily tell the differences between textures and shapes.

In short, the brain damaged child needs exposure, as soon as possible, to all forms of active visual-motor experience. He needs random exploratory movements, such as crawling, walking, rolling balls, or feeling things of different temperatures and textures.

After the looking and reaching stage, all new experiences will add to his understanding of the visual world. But he needs more than just random experience. Structured activities will speed up visual-motor development. We have discussed the "look and reach" games and the "run and fetch" games. Rolling, throwing, and catching balls will also establish focus and directionality. When the child looks where he rolls the ball, he gets it to the other person playing with him. When he watches the ball, he can catch it.

Drawing and scribbling, piling of blocks, and so on, help the child learn that what his hand does determines the line on the paper or whether the block stays on the pile. Learning this will be a long process, and the EARLIER the experience that the brain damaged child has, the better off he will be in terms of his future perceptual development.

After a discussion such as this, it will probably occur to the reader that we have only discussed the difficulties in VISUAL perception. There are also difficulties involving auditory perception and tactile (touch) perception, which shall be discussed in the following sections.

Auditory Perceptual Problems

Discrimination of sounds begins at a gross level in early infancy. The normal baby learns to distinguish first between background sounds and the human voice. This learning is largely due to the association between the sounds of a voice and the presence of food or other physical rewards. The mother of a young baby "naturally" talks to her child while caring for him. The bottle or breast is accompanied by words telling him it is time to eat. The diaper change is accompanied by words. All the daily activities are bathed in a flow of words, perceived by the normal infant as a flow of pleasing sound. The baby thus associates the sound of a voice with pleasure, and learns to listen for it. He selects voices out of the welter of sounds with which his ears are assaulted.

Next, he learns to distinguish his mother's voice from other voices. After he is five or six months old, he begins cooing. He becomes aware of his own voice and soon knows it from his mother's. At this age, a normal baby can discriminate between known and unknown voices. Indeed, a strange voice may make him scream with terror. This is often the explanation for the six- to nine-month-old baby who screams at a visit to the doctor or an infrequent visit from grandma.

By the end of the first year, some of the sounds he is producing himself will begin to be rewarded by his mother, because they sound to her like recognizable words (such as "mama"). At this point, the vocalizations may just sound like words; they are not yet. But soon the baby learns to discriminate between those sounds he makes that please his mother and those that do not. He begins narrowing his vocabulary of sounds to include only those for which he is rewarded, and thus, "real" speech is begun.

As the child grows older, he learns to discriminate finer speech sounds — words. He learns to differentiate between sounds that are very similar. Because the discrimination is rewarded by his understanding of the meaning of the utterance, he is consistently directed toward finer and finer discriminations on an auditory level. He develops a keen auditory sense.

Here, too, as with vision, the information from his hearing is augmented and clarified by other senses. Environmental noises that may be ambiguous, such as the difference between thunder and a drum roll, are easily discriminated, once the visual cues are added to the auditory ones.

As with vision, there are responses that become automatic, which are keyed by hearing. A simple example here is the immediate response any older child or adult makes when the phone rings. On a higher level, we could cite the way a driver automatically moves to the side of the road when he hears a siren behind him. A still higher automatized response to sound is the automatic response of "fine" to the sound perceived as "How are you?" All of these examples of auditory-motor responses.

We have seen the course of normal development. Here again, as with visual perception, brain damage can interfere greatly with this course.

Many brain damaged children suffer from what can be thought of as figure-ground disturbance of hearing. The brain damaged child may have extreme difficulty in separating the figure component (speech, for example) from the ground of noises surrounding it. These disturbances associated with brain damage can be greatly increased by a phenomenon of the disturbed mother-child relationship, often occuring in the families of brain damaged children.

Very often, the mother of a brain damaged baby stops talking to her baby the way mothers of normal children talk to theirs. The difficulties in feeding, diapering, and dressing are often so severe that there is little time or inclincation on the part of the mother for such talking. Mothers of brain damaged children often report that they don't remember when they stopped talking to the baby, but they "just did."

Usually the reason for this is the fact that the baby doesn't appear to respond to the sound of the mother's voice. Because of auditory perceptual difficulties, singing and soft speech doesn't calm the baby or please him. He doesn't smile when he hears his mother's voice (possibly because he cannot pick it out of the other noises surrounding it.)

Sometimes, as stated above, the mother is just too busy trying to care for a severely handicapped infant to find time to talk to him. But for whatever reason, the lack of association between the sound of a voice and pleasant caretaking experiences can lead to further failure of discriminative development. This continues into the cooing and babbling stage, if and when it occurs. The child may not discriminate between voices and environmental sounds. Therefore, he certainly can't discriminate between the different sounds he makes. Accordingly, whether or not he is praised for "speech," he will have great difficulty telling the sounds which are like speech from those which are not.

Later on, it may be difficult for him to understand spoken communication due to a failure to discriminate between the various speech sounds. At this point, the child may still find it difficult to tell speech from background noises.

Obviously, the brain damaged child needs experience in hearing all sorts of sounds, from the grossest environmental noises to the finest speech sounds. He will need to be taught first to attend to a sound. He must be rewarded for recognizing the basic difference between noise and not-noise. With the child who is nearly two years of age, this can be done with a simple but highly pleasant game. The child hides his eyes and a noise, such as the slamming of a door or the dropping of a book, is made. The child is asked to indicate WHEN he hears the sound.

The next step is very gross sound differences. With the same basic game, the child is asked not just to respond to the sounds but to identify the sound (by pointing to the door or block, or in any manner that is practical for him). He should not be asked to reproduce the sound, as this is a perceptual-motor act, which is at a higher level. Voice can be naturally introduced here, among the repertoire of sounds presented. Gradually, different voices, varying in pitch and loudness, and so on, can be added, along with environmental sounds requiring finer discriminations.

Still finer sounds should be added next. A good game at this point is to use different animal sounds, which the child must associate with the picture or name of the appropriate animal. Different musical instruments can be presented, with the child pointing to the appropriate one. Next using instruments, the child can be taught to discriminate between high and low notes.

From here, training can begin in discriminating speech sounds. Practice should begin with words that are totally different in beginning sounds. For example, one might start with a picture of a gun and a sock, and ask the child to point to the one named. When such highly different speech sounds are successfully discriminated, finer discriminations, such as "sun" and "gun," can be used. Here the beginning sounds are still quite different, but the rest of the words are identical. At a higher level, words barely differing (such as "bit and "pit" or "meat" and "mitt") can be introduced.

Up to this point, we have been discussing only the "purely perceptual" aspects of hearing — the matching and discriminating aspect. But, as with vision, the brain damaged child may have intact or nearly intact discriminative functions. The failure may be at the auditory-motor level. The difficulty here is in the automatic physical response to the auditory stimulus.

From this we could infer that apraxia can be a problem in hearing as well as vision. This is, indeed, the case, although it is not as noticeable a problem as with a visual apraxia. Let us imagine for example, a game in which a child is presented with a certain auditory pattern. The teacher claps her hands once long and twice short and fast. She asks the child to repeat this pattern. He may be unable to do so because he cannot discriminate or remember it, or both. But, assuming he can do both these things, he may still be unable to reproduce the pattern, because he cannot plan or organize the movements of his hand needed to so. He is demonstrating an auditory apraxia. This type of apraxia in the young child can, as with vision, lead to more serious primary problems in later life. Here again the child hasn't any constancy between the information received from one of his senses (in this case, his hearing) and what happens when he responds to that information. Because of this lack of constancy and stability, he has difficulty in establishing his relationship to the world he hears. (This is parallel to the problems of the child with visual apraxia.)

Training for auditory apraxia should start with very simple auditory response games. The basic discrimination games described above can be adapted for this work, by having the child reproduce what he hears. Simple rhythm games, such as the reproduction of clapped patterns, marching to beat, and marching to music. At the beginning, of course, the materials presented should be very simple. When success has been consistent with very simple patterns, the child can go on to more complex ones.

At this point, it is important to note that throughout all the training described above, the child should be made aware that sound has meaning, that there is an intrinsic value in learning to distinguish one sound from another.

If the child has had language learning experiences in a preschool situation, this should be clear to him, in terms of speech sounds. If he has not had a preschool experience, he should be helped to understand the value of speech discrimination. This can be done at home by the mother talking to him and expecting a response from him.

The same value also exists for other sounds than speech. The child will need to learn, for example, that a sharp honking of a car means he should get out of the road.

The discussion of difficulties in and training for auditory perception could become a book in itself. It is hoped that this brief covering of the topic will serve to open up the problem for further thought and questions on the part of parents.

Problems in Tactile Perception

Problems in tactile ("touch") perception are quite common in childhood brain damage. The normal infant and child gain much needed information through their tactile perceptions. The baby, in a sense, learns about love through touch. He learns to associate his mother's touch with all sorts of pleasant experiences, such as feeding and being kept dry. He feels safe and secure by being held closely and even by being wrapped securely when sleeping.

As he grows older he uses his hands to explore the world. Almost everything he sees, he touches. The crawling child is a notorious "toucher." The child learns about size and shape through games of piling, stacking, and by being able to put small objects into larger ones (as well as by NOT being able to put large objects into smaller ones).

He develops a stable sense of touch and learns to augment what he sees by what things feel like. For instance, when we spoke of distinguishing between uncast glass and a lump of ice, touch tells that the ice is cold and wet, while the glass is cool and dry.

The brain damaged child doesn't always receive correct tactile information. He may be unable to integrate how things look with how they feel. For example, if the normal child closes his eyes and feels a ball and then a cube, he can look at both objects and tell which one he has just felt. The brain damaged child may be unable to do this. He may be unable to perceive the tactile differences between sharp edges and round smoothness. Or he may be able to do this but unable to associate the tactile differences with the visual ones. For the brain damaged infant, touch may not be a clear-cut comforter for him as it is for the normal baby. In the first place, the brain damaged child often is unaware of being touched, or if aware, unable to tell WHERE he is being touched. If you touch the arm, face, and so on, of a brain damaged child who has his eyes closed, he may be unable to tell you or show you WHERE you touched him. He may be unable to respond WHEN you touch him. Therefore, it is easy to understand that as a baby, he didn't (he couldn't) build up the associations of touch and comfort so important for a healthy mother-child relationship.

Indeed, many mothers of brain damaged children find that their infants, rather than being comforted and soothed by being held, are upset and frightened by this contact. The mother, who instinctively wants to cuddle and stroke her baby, is quickly distressed by the fact that the baby screams, flinches, and actively fights her touch. The mother-child relationship, which is mainly tactual at this stage, is severely threatened again.

This is an example of what is called "tactile defensiveness." Such children often cannot bear being touched and are highly distressed by physical contact. As older children, they learn to judge when they are about to be touched and go to great lengths to avoid it. For example, many of these children are afraid of being approached from behind by a teacher, while sitting at their desks. They fear that they will be touched without being able to see the approaching contact in time to withdraw. In one extreme case, a child approached from behind by a teacher became so defensive that she upset her desk in an effort to escape the contact she feared might come.

It is easy to see from the above that brain damaged children with tactile problems need specialized training to overcome them. The occupational therapist must help them to know WHEN they are being touched and WHERE they are being touched. They need help in associating feel with sight. In the case of the tactilely defensive child, he needs to build a tolerance to more and more touch, beginning with very structured tactile situations.

It is interesting to note here that the child with tactile defensiveness is usually "tactilely blind" also. Such children are unable to get needed information from touch. The child described earlier who upset her desk to avoid the possibility of being touched is also a compulsive toucher. She wants to handle everything, particularly textured and soft objects, such as hair and cloth. She constantly asks "How does it feel?" when introduced to a new object in her environment (usually this question occurs AFTER she has felt it).

Training in touch tolerance and discrimination often go hand in hand (no pun intended). As the child learns more about the world through touch, he is often able to tolerate more physical contact.

General Rigidities in the Brain Damaged Child

This term is used to describe a number of behaviors that demonstrate any adverse reaction to change. The child with general rigidities often has great trouble adjusting to new situations or small alterations in old ones. The child gets greatly upset by changes in daily routine. He functions well only by adhering to a routine. This is true both in terms of time and space. The child is not only disturbed by time changes in his routine, such as a change in the time for dinner, but he is disturbed by changes in his physical world, such as the redecoration of his bedroom.

The child with conceptual rigidity finds it hard to change from one task to another. A response that was successful in one task is often attempted in order to solve a different task, even if the response is no longer appropriate. This is not a case of perseveration, repeating a single response when a different one is needed. Rather, it is a case of repeating a single type of response, where a different type of response is needed. For example, a child who is practicing printing letters may perseverate on "c" when asked to print "c" ("c" is taught first). The child displaying rigidity will continue printing letters when asked to draw circles or squares, even when the teacher has demonstrated the new response. (It is for this reason that two pencil-using tasks, such as printing and drawing, should never be taught in a row.)

A child with spatial rigidities becomes very upset by things often unnoticed by the normal person, such as a crooked venetian blind, or a book placed askew on a bookshelf. It is important to note that the disturbance is different from hyperirritable attention, discussed earlier. The hyperattentive child will react to a physical change in his surroundings by random, compulsive, driven activity, such as walking around and touching the new furniture in the room. The rigid child will attempt to change the situation so as to satisfy his need for order. He will, perhaps, move the book back to its proper position. If he is not allowed to do this, he may then become restless and hyperactive, or a catastrophic reaction may occur.

A child with temporal rigidity (problems with changes in time sequences) may be distressed by changes in his routine necessitated by a visit to the doctor, company in the home, or a new baby. This problem can be helped by preparing the child for the coming change and explaining to him what will happen and how the routine will be altered.

Initiatory Confusion and Delay

In the brain damaged child, the injuries that make for organizational difficulties also can affect rapidity of response. Therefore, the brain damaged child often shows slowness and confusion in "initiating" or starting to respond. The child is capable of responding to a particular stimulus, such as a visual cue or a verbal question, but there may be a considerable lag between the stimulus and the response. This is not a problem of a delay caused by decreased sensitivity to a stimulus. The problem is one of slowness in organizing and committing a proper response. The child may be quite capable of telling you, for example, that the color of the block you are holding is red. However, he may appear to look perfectly blank for a few seconds and seem not to know the answer. He hasn't "forgotten" the color name. It just takes him longer than a normal child to recognize the question, pick out the answer, and organize the motor response needed to give the answer.

It is important to know that the brain damaged child needs extra organizing time. If, before this time has elapsed, a command is repeated, he will lose his place in the organization of the response and have to begin all over again. The process of organizing a response may take the brain damaged child from fifteen to forty-five seconds. Therefore, when a parent asks his child a question or gives him a command, it is a good prescription to state the question or command and wait up to forty-five seconds. If no answer has been made, the command or question should be repeated and another forty-five second interval allowed to elapse. If, after this point, no response has been made, it should be assumed that the command or question is beyond the child's capacities, at this particular moment in time, or that the child is willfully ignoring the command.

CHAPTER FOUR

HELPING THE
BRAIN DAMAGED CHILD AT HOME

The Need for Structure

In the previous chapters, the underlying implication for home management was always present. For the child with attention problems, for the child with rigidities, in short, for the brain damaged child, structure is vital if a sane home life for the entire family is to be achieved.

"Structure," however, is a frightening word to many parents. They see it as being a rigid, cold, unfeeling "program." Structure needn't be prison-like or army-like. The distinction here is between structure and regimentation. Structure is the creation of an environment and the control of the environment so that a child can better cope with various situations. Regimentation is doing the same thing in the same way every day without change because this is the way it is done. Structure shouldn't be and indeed can't be inflexible. Home routines must leave allowance for special occasions, family crises, and last minute changes in plans. But, there must be a daily pattern in the life of the brain damaged child. It should perhaps be considered here that if the child is unable to cope with any unexpected changes in home routine, even when prepared for them, the home may not be the place for his maximal improvement.

The brain damaged child's many problems previously discussed can make insurmountable obstacles out of everyday matter-of-fact jobs like getting ready for school. If as many areas in his life as possible can be automatized, such obstacles can be less formidable. If the child knows what is coming next, what is expected of him, and how he is supposed to react, the level of propositionality involved in daily tasks can be decreased. Scheduling of daily living routines in a dependable and predictable pattern, thus reducing the tendency toward confusion and anxiety encountered by the brain damaged child will result in a more peaceful life for the entire family. When any change in routine is necessitated, this too can be made as easy as possible, if the child is given warning of the impending change and told what will happen (or be expected of him) in place of the normal routine.

Sometimes, when particular routines have become automatized, and the parent expects a change, behavioral problems occur because she doesn't change the language of her command to the child sufficiently for him to recognize that change is expected of him. For example, the mother of one of our children at the clinic told her son to get ready for a bath one evening (a routine change, since he normally bathed in the morning) and was upset to discover that he came down to say good night, dressed for bed. He was very pleased with himself and her disapproval precipitated a major catastrophic reaction. On questioning the parent, she related that she told her son to "go upstairs and get undressed." When asked what she normally tells him to do in preparation for going to bed, she replied, "Go upstairs and get undressed for bed." The command language was so similar that the child was totally unprepared for the expected change in routine. The tantrum that followed could have been avoided had the child been told, "Tonight you are going to have a bath before you go to bed. Go upstairs and take off your clothes." Thus, the command heralds the change.

It is important to remember that the brain damaged child needs not only temporal structure (scheduling of activities) but spatial structure as well. We have previously discussed the nonstimulating environment that is initially needed for the hyperattentive and hyperactive child. Obviously, the entire house cannot be arranged in such a manner. Plain bare walls and lack of ornamentation of any kind would make the rest of the family feel as though they were living in a barracks. However, it is important to remember that to the young brain damaged child the normal living room, with its pictures on the walls, knick-knacks on the tables, brightly colored magazines, and patterned or textured upholstery, is a chaotic, terrifying, and unbelievably overstimulating place. He needs a retreat from such a room, when he finds he is unable to cope with it. His room — HIS OWN ROOM, is a real necessity for this reason — must be a quiet, calm, nonstimulating place. The walls and floors should be plain. The bedspreads and curtains should be solid colors. Adequate storage of toys, books, and clothing is a must. These things must be out of sight, behind doors or curtains. In short, the room should offer the child a blessed rest from the frightening welter of stimuli found in the normal household. As he becomes older and has more control of his attention, he may request some alteration in the bareness of his room. This can be tried, at such a time as he feels ready to handle it, but he should be allowed to change his mind if necessary. The haven of his plain room should be open to him for as long as he needs it.

During the discussion of spatial rigidities, we mentioned the difficulty the brain damaged child often has with any change in the placement of furniture, and so forth, in the house. Obviously, keeping the furniture in the exact same spot all the time (not to mention the ashtrays, books, et cetera) is more than any normal family can tolerate. Invariably, some piece of furniture or some household ornament gets moved, perhaps imperceptively to the rest of the family.

Suddenly, for no apparent reason, the spatially-rigid child may become agitated. This may be a reaction to a misplaced object in the room. It can be returned to its place, but this will only alleviate the momentary problem. If decreasing his rigidity is the goal, have the child move the misplaced object back to its normal spot. Then say "I think I like it better somewhere else" and have HIM move it to a new place. If this procedure is done consistently whenever spatial rigidity causes a problem, the child will begin to cope with this difficulty.

Redecorating the home or rearranging the furniture can be upsetting to any brain damaged child, not just the spatially-rigid one. When the step is taken, the child should be present at the change and help participate in the actual moving. This is true whether the change is in his room or in any other room in the home. The change should NEVER be made while he is asleep or in school.

The child's participation in a major furniture move is extremely important in preventing severe catastrophic reactions. At our clinic, when a furniture rearrangement was planned by our preschool teacher, it had to be done three times: once by the teacher alone to determine how she wanted the furniture arranged. The furniture was then returned to its original position and the morning preschool group helped move it to the new position; the furniture was again returned to the old position during the lunch hour and finally the afternoon group was able to help move it during their class time. This may sound like a great deal of work but it saved the teacher (and the children) much stress in adjustment reactions to an unexpected change.

Management of Daily Routines at Home

During our discussion of life with a brain damaged child, it became apparent that three large conflict areas existed daily between parent and child. The main conflicts of the day occur during feeding, dressing, and toileting. Structuring of these three routines can make the home life of the brain damaged child and his family much more successful.

Much of the problems in eating involve a time factor. Many mothers of brain damaged children state that breakfast is the worst meal of the day, making the day start off abysmally. This may be due in a large part to the fact that the brain damaged child, regardless of how early he awakens, is a "slow starter," finding it difficult to leave sleep and even more difficult to organize himself neurologically for the day ahead. The act of eating breakfast requires him to be more alert and organized than he may be capable of being, first thing in the morning. It may be easier for him to eat breakfast if he has had time to orient himself to the new day beforehand. Postponing breakfast so that it is not one of the first acts entered into after waking can help make the meal more pleasant. It may help, for instance, to wake the child ten minutes early and allow him to lie in bed quietly for this period. Some children make their own adaptation to early morning difficulties. The child may get up before the rest of the family and play a record or engage in a nonuseful activity such as spinning the wheels of a toy truck. After this he is ready to start the day. With other children, the parent must give them this period of orientation.

For some children, even such an orientation interval before breakfast will not be sufficient to ready them for breakfast eating. In this case, it is suggested that the mother offer the child something like fortified milk (perhaps a glass of instant breakfast or an eggnog). This is as nourishing as a normal breakfast, and the child will rarely refuse milk the way he will a big breakfast. For this child, perhaps lunch can be a bigger meal than just soup or a sandwich. The daily egg may be better accepted at lunch than at breakfast. If the child doesn't want to eat a larger lunch, the liquid breakfast and small lunch can be supplement by a ten o'clock snack, a three o'clock snack, or both.

Problems with solid food also contribute to mealtime difficulties. When the child is receiving speech and language therapy, any problems he has in chewing, sucking, or swallowing will be worked on in the course of his therapy. The therapist may request that the child drink milk through a straw several times a day at home and may give the parent specific instructions on chewing training and straw drinking. One such program will be discussed in a later section. However, coordination of therapy and home programs in this area should do a great deal to alleviate this mealtime problem.

The above discussion of chewing, sucking, and swallowing problems referred to the child with organic problems, caused by their physical handicap, such as cerebral palsy. However, unless the child has organic problems markedly interferring with swallowing, confirmed by the pediatrician, hard foods should be a regular part of his diet. The child who for other reasons refuses hard foods must learn to eat them, not only for nutritional reasons but because lack of chewing prevents adequate development of the reflexes and muscles of speech.

The question here is how to get the child to accept hard foods. This can be done gradually by mixing some finely chopped solid foods with baby or junior food. At the beginning, there should only be a very slight proportion of the solid food and the consistency should be gradually built up until it is mostly table food.

Many parents do not recognize that refusal of solids is a major part of their child's feeding problem. They will report that all their child will eat is hamburger, mashed potatoes, ice cream, pudding, and perhaps scrambled eggs. The food dislikes of the child include all meats but hamburger (and perhaps chicken) and all vegetables. The child will eat the middle of a piece of bread, but not the crust, even on soft white bread. This is the typical picture of a child who is refusing hard foods, not just a finicky eater.

For the brain damaged child with attention problems, some physical aspects of mealtimes may need to be changed. We are used to pretty tables with flowered or patterned tablecloths, lots of silverware and dishes, and all sorts of foods on the table at the same time. But consider what this mass of objects could do the hyperirritable attention of a brain damaged child. He might never be able to concentrate on his food long enough to eat it. This can explain the playing with silverware, picking at different foods, and reaching for objects (and consequent spilling of milk or water) that so often make chaos of his and his parents' meals.

A plain-colored tablecloth with a bright, solid-color place mat in front of his place will help the brain damaged child to focus his attention on his plate. Extra dishes and silver not being used for the course at hand can be kept off the table and out of his sight. He will do much better at eating if he has only the utensils he needs to eat the food in front of him.

For some children, the stimulation of the whole family at the dinner table with several running conversations going on simultaneously is far too exciting to allow for eating. These children may need to have their meals quietly and alone, with the same aids to attending to the meal as described above. When the routine of mealtime is finally established, dinner with one other family member, perhaps an older sibling, could be tried. Eventually of course, the goal is to have the brain damaged child eating with his family and functioning as a family member.

However, before the child is isolated from the family at mealtimes, a long trial period of meals with the family should be tried. In most cases, it is easier to put up with a few mishaps and tantrums in the beginning and to have the child accustomed from the start to functioning at meals with other people. If isolation is necessary, the road back to family dinners is very difficult.

This brings us to the social and behavioral problems of dinner, which is more than just a meal, like breakfast and lunch. Dinner is a social occasion as well as a time for eating. Very often the brain damaged child creates a behavioral problem because he feels excluded by the family from the dinner conversation. This can be handled easily by sitting the child next to his father. When the child appears about to start a commotion, the father can place his hand on the child, giving him the attention he wants. Conversation intended for the whole family can be directed to the child. For example, daddy can say "Johnny, did you know that I sold two cars today?" This imparts the needed information to the family and also allows Johnny to feel that he is part of the family, even if he doesn't totally comprehend the content of the conversation.

If the child habitually leaves the table and meals become hour-long ordeals, it is important to remember that a healthy, well-nourished child will not suffer nutritionally by missing a meal or two. If the pediatrician feels that the child is healthy and well nourished, discipline at mealtime should be instituted. If the child leaves the table or plays with his food, assume that he is no longer hungry and take the food away. If he really hasn't eaten enough, he will be hungry and will ask for a between-meal snack. But the kitchen is closed between meals. After one or two meals or not eating and being very hungry between meals, he will learn that he must finish his dinner in the allotted time, if he is to be satisfied. This technique not only makes mealtimes easier and less hectic but teaches the child that he has certain responsibilities, that he has jobs that must be finished in a particular time, and that food is to eat and not a toy.

Granted, this seems like a very hard-hearted attitude for a parent to take. To "starve" a child and not let him eat between meals when he is hungry is a very difficult thing for a mother to do. A mother's role is traditionally that of a nurturer, a giver of the stuff of life. To most mothers, feeding their family in all important, a way of expressing love. But it must be realized that if the child was really hungry, he wouldn't be playing with his food or running away from the table. Getting that extra piece of meat or that second forkful of vegetable is really not that important in the total scheme of things. What is important is that mealtime not be a running battle and that the child learn what is expected of him at the table. When this method of mealtime discipline seems impossible for the mother to bear, it is important for her to remember that within a few days the child's natural enjoyment of food and need for food will come to the fore, and the "starvation" will end.

It should be noted here that the removal of food serves as a discipliner only for mealtime problems. The child should not be deprived of basic food for misbehaving in some other area of living. In other words, if Johnny has been naughty, he shouldn't be sent to bed without his supper. There are far more effective means of disciplining him, which will be discussed later.

Another difficulty that may occur at meals is difficulty in self-feeding. The child begins to feed himself by finger feeding with a cracker, a piece of frankfurter, and so on. At the same time, if the child is not severely physically impaired, when he is being spoon-fed, the mother can put a second spoon into the child's hand. During the feeding process, with a food he really enjoys, she can stimulate a self-feeding by becoming busy elsewhere between spoonfuls. Most children will react by beginning to use their own spoon to feed themselves.

Some children have the concept of lifting the spoon to the mouth but need help in getting the food on the spoon and turning it so the food gets into the mouth, rather than on the child's clothes. It might be easier at this point to switch the child to a fork. The child is taught to stab the food with the fork. Then when he goes to put the fork into his mouth, it doesn't have to be turned in order to keep the food from falling off. If the child is having very consistent difficulty with spoon feeding and is still willing to keep on feeding himself, that might be a way to avoid having him lose all desire to feed himself due to lack of success.

Dressing is the second daily routine that can be made simpler for both the brain damaged child and his mother. The child should be dressed quickly, routinely, and matter-of-factly but with a pleasant mother-child interchange. With the normal child, mothers play all sorts of dressing games, such as "Where is the baby?" when his head is covered by his shirt. Dressing is an ideal time for the child to learn about his body parts in an informal and enjoyable manner. This incidental learning can take the stress off the actual dressing, as well. When the child is playing a game of "Where's Johnny's hand?" as his arm and hand are put into his sleeve, he learns what his hand is and where it goes. The shirt is quickly put on. This also has the advantage of reinforcing the normal mother-child relationship, so needed in the life of the brain damaged child.

The attitude of the parent is very important here. The child reacts to the mother's feeling of tension and dressing becomes a battle. If the mother leaves adequate time in her daily schedule to allow the child to be dressed unhurriedly (or to dress himself unhurriedly), part of the battle is won.

When the child is being dressed, the most efficient position for this is to get him on the mother's lap. This allows him to see her hands and what they are doing, in the same position as his hands will be when he dresses himself. Also, it is easier to maneuver the arms and legs of a sitting child than one who is lying on a bed (it is also easier on the mother's back).

Clothing choice can be structured for the brain damaged child to make fewer decisions necessary for him when he begins dressing himself. In the beginning he should have no choice at all, until he is capable of making choices in other areas (such as whether he wants a chocolate or vanilla cookie). Where the parent makes the greatest error is in giving the child too much choice before he is capable of handling this. He should not be asked "What do you want to wear today?" but "Do you want to wear the red shirt or the green shirt?" When he is capable of dealing with this choice, the range can be widened until he can make an entirely free choice on his own.

Even when the child is making all his own clothing choices, the parent can structure things so that his choices will be appropriate. He can be taught the appropriate clothing to be worn for different seasons or weather and for different occasions. If he learns and is told regularly that jeans, for example, are the proper clothing to be worn for playing outdoors, he will be less likely to create a family crisis by dirtying his Sunday suit just before it is time to go to church. However, if each day his mother chooses the

appropriate clothing and merely gives it to him, without helping
him to associate the particular type of clothing with the occasion
or weather, he will not learn to choose the proper clothing
himself.

Incidentally, often the morning is too hectic for all this decision
making to be done effectively, especially in view of the difficulties
the brain damaged child has in functioning in the morning. It is far
easier on all concerned to establish clothing choice as part of the
bedtime routine, choosing the clothing and laying it out in a
particular, established place.

When the child is ready to begin undressing and dressing himself
(undressing comes first developmentally), he can be helped to
learn these skills if his clothing is selected on a practical basis. The
clothing should be sized so that it is large enough for the child to
put it on easily and allow for freedom of motion. Sometimes,
particularly with a physically handicapped child whose arm and
hand control is poor, this may mean sacrificing an ideally fitting
garment for a looser one; but most parents would agree that
increasing the child's independence is worth this.

Front openings, for ease of fastening and unfastening, will also
speed the dressing and undressing processes. A clear definition of
the front and back is also helpful (as well as the inside and outside
of the garment).

The child with tactile defensiveness may have some special
problems with clothing that can be alleviated by proper selection.
They often dislike turtleneck shirts, tight wristbands, and other
constricting features in clothing (such as an elastic waist). They
may also be disturbed by loosely-fitting shoes such as loafers and
be more secure with tightly-laced oxfords or sneakers. Belts that
hold trousers securely, but without constriction, are also good
here. The tactilely defensive child is disturbed by things rubbing
and slipping on his body, so that the tight shoes and the belt will
alleviate this problem.

The third problem area in daily living is toilet training. The big
question here is who is going to be trained — the mother or the
child. When someone speaks of a child who is trained at a very
early age, such as at one year, the mother, not the child, is trained.
Obviously, the goal should be to train the child.

Firstly, the child must feel physically secure on the toilet seat. If a regular toilet with a training seat is used, the child's feet generally do not touch the floor. This can be very frightening experience to a young child. A small stool on which to rest his feet while seated on the toilet will help him to feel more comfortable.

For bowel training, a reasonably consistent pattern is necessary. The child should move his bowels at the same approximate time each day. If it is in the morning one day, in the evening the next and in the afternoon the third day, he is not ready to be trained, and a three-month interval should be allowed to elapse before setting up a schedule.

When he is consistent, he is ready. Hopefully, the time he chooses will be in the morning, right after lunch, or before bedtime, because the mother needs to have at least fifteen minutes with the child each day for the training procedure.

At the chosen time, the child should be calm and relaxed. He should be taken to a room adjacent to the bathroom and a quiet activity should be undertaken by mother and child. A story is a good activity. Soft music, barely audible, can be played also. Nothing exciting should occur.

Then the mother fills a rectal syringe with three or four ounces of warm water and inserts it into the child's anus. We are not advocating an enema here; this is just enough liquid to give the child the sensation of a full bowel and to make him want to expel it.

When he feels uncomfortable, he is toileted and given the verbal signal for bowel movement. When he moves his bowels, he is told "good boy, you _____!" After three days of consistent bowel movement associated with the verbal signal, it is time to begin reducing the amount of liquid by one half to one ounce. This reduction continues to the point where the syringe is empty, but it is still held to the anus for the length of time it formerly took to insert the three to four ounces. Then the child is toileted. The empty syringe associated with the verbal signal continues for a three-day period. On the fourth day, after the quiet activity, the parent takes down the child's pants, takes him to the bathroom where the syringe is clearly visible, and gives him the verbal signal. By now, the child may already be signaling to the mother. When he moves his bowels with just the verbal signal, training is accomplished.

From now on, the child will attempt to verbalize an approximation of the family signals. When he does this, the mother should say "Oh, you want to_____" and toilet him. It is important to recognize his approximation of the toileting words. Very often, toileting difficulties from this point on are not failures of the child to signal but failures of the parents to recognize that the child is signaling.

Discipline in the Home

During the discussion of the emotional content of the home, it should have become clear that enlightened discipline is of the utmost importance for the brain damaged child. In order for the child to function as a family member, as a class member and later, as a member of society, he must learn that there are rules to be obeyed.

Enlightened discipline is the key here. A child should never be punished for an infringement of a rule he is incapable of comprehending. The first thing to be determined is whether or not the child is aware of misbehaving. If he is not, rather than discipline he needs to be taught what is expected of him and why (to the extent that he can comprehend).

Once this aspect is settled, the question of how to discipline becomes important. We believe it is safe to state that almost any method of discipline that is effective (barring techniques that are physically abusive to the child) is adequate. In different families and for different children, different techniques work. Some older children, particularly those with average or superior intelligence, respond well to reasoning and spoken reprimands. Some children, especially quite young ones, who must be stopped from some behavior such as touching a hot stove, will respond best to a slap on the hand.

Another technique which works well with brain damaged children is the "punishment chair." A small chair is set aside to be used specifically when the child misbehaves. When this occurs, the chair is moved to the center of the room and the child is told he is to stay there for an allotted period of time, with no diversions (the television set is off). Very often he is told that the period is fifteen minutes, but in actuality five minutes is adequate. The chair is placed in the center of the room rather than facing a corner because the child can devise interesting diversions for himself in a corner that are not available in the open center of the room. There is no wall to touch, paint to peel, and so forth, and he is in full view of his parents.

If he refuses to stay in the chair, a scarf can be used to anchor him to the chair, tied loosely enough so as not to constrict him but tightly enough so that he cannot get free unassisted.

It is important to note here that this chair is meant for major, purposeful infringements of rules. For lesser misdemeanors, he may be forbidden to watch television or deprived of something he desires.

One of the important things to remember when disciplining a child is WHAT is being labeled a punishment. We do not feel, for example, that a child should be sent to bed for misbehaving. Bed is a place where a child must go every night (and every afternoon, if he is still napping) regardless of whether he is behaving well or poorly. To make bed punishment causes terrific bedtime problems, when no punishment is meant.

The same thing is true for basic meals. Meals are something the child should know he will always receive, so long as he eats them. They should not be contingent upon behavior. Note that the keynote here is BASIC meals. This does not mean that snacks, candy, or cake cannot be withheld for misbehavior, if this is effective with a particular child. Our personal bias is not in favor of this technique because its converse assumes that sweets are a reward (if lack of them is a punishment). Candy and sweets are things to which a child need never be introduced, and making them a reward gives them undue importance.

In short, whatever any parent finds that is effective and fair with his or her child is acceptable, so long as the discipline is consistent. The biggest error made in disciplining is being inconsistent. If a child is punished for a forbidden behavior sometimes and the behavior is ignored at other times, he will never be certain that the behavior is undesirable.

Early Linguistic Training for Preschool Readiness

A very important factor in the early stages of speech development is practice in the use of muscles and reflexes which are used in speaking. In many aspects, these are the same muscles and reflexes used in eating and drinking. Many brain damaged children have difficulty in using these mechanisms and need help in developing them. In some ways, the muscular activity of chewing, sucking, and swallowing is similar to the muscular activity of speaking. Therefore, as soon as it is feasible, and certainly by the second year, children should get as much practice as possible in chewing and swallowing small bits of hard food. Often, it is a good practice to begin with something like zweiback or hard toast. In the beginning, it is wise to soften these foods in milk or water. As the child's ability to chew improves, the foods should be given progressively less softened and finally, completely dry. Sucking activities, such as drinking liquids from a straw, also helps develop some of the muscles and reflexes used in speaking.

Another very important aspect in language development is how much language the child hears. We have stated the importance of the mother establishing a good relationship with her child, talking to him during caretaking activities, in the same way as a mother does with a normal child. However, as well as being crucial to the mother-child relationship, this conversational approach is needed in terms of the child's developing language. The child learns about his body from things his mother says about his body while she dresses him. His understanding of language grows as he learns to associate familiar objects with words.

Soon he begins making sucking movements when mother says, "I'll get your bottle." He lifts his arms up when his mother says, "Give me your arm for this sleeve." The normal child learns to comprehend language in this way. The brain damaged child must have the same informal language experiences in order to profit from the language-oriented training he will receive in a preschool setting. In order to function at the preschool level, he must have previous language experiences like this in the home.

It is also important for the brain damaged child to participate in the language-oriented games a mother plays with a child. "How big is the baby?" "pat-a-cake," or "peek-a-boo" all teach the child to discern the auditory patterns and to learn the proper responses (raising of the arms, covering the eyes, et cetera) to the different patterns.

The important thing to realize here is that it is this informal conversation that the child hears from his mother that teaches him value of discrimination and comprehending speech. Children must be motivated to learn language. If the mother gestures to the child or automatically does things for him without verbal accompaniment, he will never need to understand language.

Babbling is an important antecedent to speech. When the child begins cooing and makes babbling sounds, he needs reinforcement for this activity, so that he will continue. With some children, the mother's pleasure at the sounds will be enough to elicit more sounds from them. But for other children, more specific reinforcement is necessary. If the mother repeats the babbling sounds as the baby makes them, he is reinforced. This will lead him to continue making sounds and to increase the frequency of these sounds. The child gets great pleasure out of his mother repeating his sounds, and this eventually leads to his attempts to repeat the speech sounds he hears her make.

The mother of a normal child does this naturally when her baby begins making the adorable "ooh" and "ah" sounds of infancy, and her baby quickly responds to this. However, with the brain damaged child, cooing is sometimes rare, and the baby doesn't noticeably respond to the mother cooing back at him. Unconsciously, because she gets no response from her baby, the mother ceases babbling back to him. It is important that she NOT cease, but continue to babble back to the baby whenever he babbles, regardless of his response. If she keeps this up consistently, the baby will eventually begin increasing his babbling and be more attentive to sound in general.

In order for a child to learn to speak, one of the prerequisites is motivation. The child must learn that speech is functional and has real value to him. The parents who anticipate their child's every wish provide him with no need to learn language. The child whose gestural language is completely understood sees no need to learn spoken language. The child must begin to see that his needs will not be met without speech of some sort.

A good way of teaching the need to speak to a young brain damaged child is to make it necessary for him to vocalize (make sounds) in order to get what he wants. This is not as difficult as requiring actual speech from a speechless child. It merely requires that he make a vocal sound, for which he is rewarded.

This can be done in many ways. The child may have to "coo" before getting his bottle or a favorite toy. A game of rolling the ball may incorporate this training. The child only gets the ball when he "asks for it."

As the child is pointing or gesturing to get something, the parent can say, "I don't understand you unless you talk" and insist that he make a sound before giving him the wanted object.

This requires a certain amount of patience and persistence on the part of the parents, but the result is well worth it. Gradually, the child comes to see that not only is listening and comprehending his parents' speech of value to him but that trying to speak himself is also valuable.

In order for the brain damaged child to function in a preschool setting, where much of his important language learning takes place, he must be able to follow simple commands. This can be learned at home in informal games and small tasks that young children really enjoy. The child can learn to stand up, sit down, and lie down on command. He can be taught to fetch his coat, shoes, boots, or hat. He can learn a simple noun vocabulary through a command game of "Bring me the _____." This can start out in a very structured fashion, with two or three familiar objects in a row and the child asked to fetch one of them. The list of objects can expand with the increase in his vocabulary. Other command games involving touching objects in the environment will also build his vocabulary and increase his abilities to follow commands. Language comprehension at this level is an important skill to learn. For most brain damaged children it can be learned most efficiently at home.

It is hoped that the home management techniques and ideas mentioned in this chapter will stimulate the parents of brain damaged children to creative thinking about ways in which to best help their child overcome his problem in the home.

In this book, we have tried to give parents some understanding of the problems of young brain damaged children, as well as some techniques for dealing with these problems. We want to emphasize, however, that diagnosis and effective therapeutic treatment of such children is the domain of the physicians, psychologists, trained therapists, and educators who have special professional knowledge of these problems.

BIBLIOGRAPHY

1. Berko, M. J.: Mental evaluation of the aphasic child. Amer J Occup Ther, V:241-43, 1951.
2. Berko, M. J.: Psychometric scatter: Its application in the clinical prediction of future mental development in cases of childhood brain injury. Cereb Palsy Rev, XVI:2, 16-18, 1955.
3. Berko, M. J.: Some factors in the mental evaluation of cerebral palsied children. Cereb Palsy Rev, XI:6, 11, 15, 1953.
4. Berko, M. J.: Some factors in the perceptual deviations of children with cerebral palsy. Cereb Palsy Rev, XV:2, 3-4, 11, 1954.
5. Berko, M. J.: The measurement of intelligence in children with cerebral palsy. J Pediat, XLVII:252-60, 1955.
6. Berko, M. J., and Berko, F. G.: Implications of language difficulties in the cerebral palsied adults. Cereb Palsy Rev, XIV:9, 11, 14, 1953.
7. Bice, H. V.: Psychological examination of the cerebral palsied. J Excep Child, XIV:163-68, 1948.
8. Birch, H. G. (Ed.): Brain Damage in Children. The Biological and Social Aspects. Baltimore, Williams & Wilkins, 1964.
9. Clark, R. M.: The child with unsuspected brain injury. Talk XXXVI:6-9, 1955.
10. Cardwell, V. E.: Cerebral Palsy — Advances in Understanding and Care. New York, Association for Crippled Children, 1956.
11. Cruickshank, W. M.: A Teaching Method for Brain Damaged and Hyperactive Children. Syracuse, Syracuse University Press, 1961.
12. Cruickshank, W. M.: The Brain Injured Child in Home, School and Community. Syracuse, Syracuse University Press, 1967.
13. Cruickshank, W. M., Bice, H. V., and Wollen, N. E.: Perception and Cerebral Palsy. Syracuse, Syracuse University Press, 1957.
14. Cruickshank, W. M., and Raus, G. M.: Cerebral Palsy. Syracuse, Syracuse University Press, 1955.
15. Dolphin, J. E., and Cruickshank, W. M.: Visual-motor perception in children with cerebral palsy. Quart J Child Behav, III:198-209, 1951.
16. Gesell, A., et al.: The First Five Years. New York, Harper & Row, 1949.
17. Lewis, R. S., Strauss, A. A., and Lehtinen, L. E.: The Other Child. New York, Grune & Stratton, 1960.
18. Mecham, M. J., Berko, M. J., and Berko, F. G.: Speech Therapy in Cerebral Palsy. Springfield, Charles C Thomas, 1960.
19. Mecham, M. J., Berko, M. J., Berko, F. G., and Palmer, M. F.: Communication Training in Childhood Brain Damage. Springfield, Charles C Thomas, 1966.
20. Spock, B., and Lerrige, M. C.: Caring for Your Disabled Child. Greenwich, Fawcett Publications, 1965.
21. Strauss, A. A., and Kephart, N. C.: Psychopathology and Education of

the Brain-injured Child: Progess in Theory and Clinic. New York, Grune & Stratton, 1955.

22. Strauss, A. A., and Lehtinen, L. E.: Psychopathology and Education of the Brain-injured Child. New York, Grune & Stratton, 1947.

GLOSSARY

AMNESIC REACTIONS: The inability to or difficulty in finding the appropriate linguistic response to the given situation, even though the child knows the response and has previously given it in similar situations. Amnesic responses are usually not thought of as being associated with propositional stress.

ANOMIA: An inability to name objects or recall and recognize names (dysnomia — impaired ability).

APHASIA: An inability to handle symbolic formulation and expression: related to both auditory and visual systems (dysphasia — impaired ability).

APRAXIA: The inability to organize a motor response where the child is able to physically perform the motor act involved, to perceive the sensory input, and to integrate his perceptions. More simply, apraxia is the inability to motor plan.

ATAXIA: A condition related to cerebellar damage, characterized by marked incoordination and disturbed equilibrium.

ATHETOSIS: A condition related to extrapyramidal damage, characterized by involuntary motion and incoordination.

AUDIDITORY DISCRIMINATION: The ability to differentiate between sounds which the person is able to "hear" and/or to draw inferences or abstract from such differences.

AUDITORY PERCEPTUAL DEVIANCE: Perceptual deviance in auditory sensory intake.

AUTISM: A condition of being dominated by subjective self-centered trends of thought or behavior, showing a paucity of social or communicative relations.

BODY SCHEME: A sensory-motor awareness of the body, how these elements are related to each other, and how the body relates to space and gravity.

CATASTROPHIC REACTION: An intensive display of emotional lability or reactive inappropriateness which appears when the child is faced with a situation which is beyond his capacity for propositional integration.

CLOSURE DRIVE: The extreme need to complete a task already begun before starting another and the need to bring a definite end to one task before requiring the child to begin another, i.e. putting away the toys before coming to supper, or erasing the arithmetic from the chalk board before beginning reading.

COGNITIVE: The faculty of knowing, of becoming aware of objects of thought or perception, including understanding and reasoning.

CONCEPTUAL RIGIDITY: A learning rather than a behavioral disability. It refers to the inability to shift from one concept or activity to another concept or activity, both of which are well within his performance level, when such shifting is appropriate. When he is required to make such an appropriate shift *without help*, the child becomes confused and disorganized. Conceptual rigidity is a form of abstracting difficulty.

CUE: Any "hint" that will enable the child to successfully perform. While this is a valuable clinical tool to overcome the child's fear of failure, there must be complete awareness that the cue is being given. It is a fact that the child *cannot* be presumed to know the response until he is able to give it without cues.

DEVIANT ABSTRACTING AND CATEGORIZING PROCESSES: A language disorder in which the child's difficulties with generalizing may vary from extreme concreteness and rigidity in concept formation to bizarre or highly unusual categorizing behavior. An example of extreme concreteness occurs when the child cannot group an apple and banana as fruit; he may group these two but may not recognize an orange as the "same type of thing," fruit; or he groups all three as belonging to the same category, because they all have to be peeled.

DISINHIBITION: The child's inability to hold back a linguistic response which is inappropriate to the immediate set or situation but not to the background environmental stimuli.

DRIFTING ATTENTION: The inability to follow through with a simple activity because of weak or brief focus of attention. (Please note that "loss of set" may be due to "drifting attention" and/or "abstracting difficulties." See definition of "set.")

EMOTIONAL LABILITY AND REACTIVE INAPPROPRIATIVENESS: "The brain damaged child is one who laughs readily, cries easily, and is prone to temper tantrums." These reactive behaviors tend at times to be inappropriate in mode of expression, in duration, and/or in intensity. They may also be inappropriate to the situation, i.e. crying at a joke or laughing uncontrollably while being reprimanded. While these responses appear to be a generalized affect disturbance, not always related to propositional stress, increased propositional stress intensifies the inappropriate emotional reactions to a marked degree.

FIGURE-GROUND DISTURBANCE: In the normal environment, there are many stimuli of each sensory modality, i.e. many noises or many things to see. The individual learns which at any given moment are important (figure) and which are to be ignored (ground) for comprehension, i.e. he "hears" the teacher's voice and does not "hear" voices in the hallway, or he "sees" the boy's picture in the book and does not "see" the pictures on the bulletin board. Many brain injured or learning disability children do not have this ability to select out of the total environmental stimuli which stimuli to attend to at any given moment. In most instances, their stimuli intake may be a combination of parts of the figure stimuli and parts of the ground stimuli which conveys no meaning. For example, if the teacher is reading a story about Jack and two people are talking in the hallway about the weather, the child may hear "Jack is . . . snowing."

GENERAL HYPERACTIVITY: A generalized excess of motor activity, compulsively driven, which is inappropriate to the situation but not to the background stimuli in the environment. It is an extreme stress reaction to the child's inability to achieve selective focus of attention.

GROSS MOTOR ACTIVITY: Any physical fitness or recreational game, requiring the use of large body muscles, which is organized and initiated by another person.

HABITUATION: Learning to do frequently-performed activities automatically. Children with learning disabilities are extremely slow in habituating.

HEMIPLEGIA: A paralysis of one side of the body.

HYPERIRRITABLE ATTENTION: The difficulty displayed by learning disability children in selecting one stimulus complex out of a broader field of stimuli. Therefore, figure-ground disturbances may be considered a form of hyperirritable attention as well as a form of perceptual deviance. The difference seems to be in the specific manifestation of the figure-ground confusion. For example, the child is telling about a picture of a boy in a pasture on a summer's day while people are talking about the wintery weather in the hallway, and the child says "The boy's hair is green," he may be showing a perceptual figure-ground disturbance due to perceptual deviance in that he is confusing the boy (figure) with the leaves on the tree (ground). But if he says "The boy is . . . snowing," then clearly the figure-ground disturbance is stemming from a form of hyperirritable attention.

INITIATORY CONFUSION AND DELAY: There is a period of time which the child needs to organize his response *before* giving any overt sign that he has heard the question or command. It varied from 15 to 45 seconds, usually around 30 seconds. If the command or question is repeated during this "organizational" interval, the repetition seems to "short-circuit" the response to the original question or command, or to confuse the child, so that he cannot give any response.

LEARNING DISABILITIES: In this context, a syndrome of minimal to moderate dysfunctions in perceptual, perceptual-motor, symbolic, and cognitive processes. These dysfunctions impede the acquisition of basic educational skills but are not necessarily associated with general mental retardation.

LOSS OF SET: A shift of task orientation when it is not appropriate. An example of this type of abstracting difficulty occurs when the child, in the middle of a line of simple addition examples which he has answered correctly thus far, begins to subtract rather than add.

MINIMAL BRAIN DAMAGE: A syndrome of mildly-manifested linguistic, symbolic, perceptual, and perceptual-motor dysfunctions in children with no overt gross motor disability. These dysfunctions appear to be milder manifestations of the same syndrome, at a more intense level, of the dysfunctions known to be associated with more severe, or clinically-palpable, brain injury. Hence, the theoretical construct of "minimal" brain damage.

MOTOR PLANNING: Any given purposeful activity in a series of motor acts of varying complexity performed in a specific sequence in order to accomplish the intended goal. Many children with learning disabilities do not have the ability to initiate such a series of activities and/or to carry them through in the appropriate sequence, even though they have the intellectual capacity, know the intended goal, and can well perform each motor act required.

PARAPLEGIA: A paralysis of one half of the body – usually the lower half.

PERCEPT: A mental impression derived both from immediate sensory experience and the mental reaction thereto.

PERCEPTUAL CONSTANCY: An ability to perceive an object as possessing invariant properties of shape and size in spite of the variability of the impression on the retinal surface because of distance or rotation.

PERCEPTUAL DYSFUNCTION-PERCEPTUAL DEVIANCE: Difficulty in the ability to respond to sensory intake as the majority of people do.

PERCEPTUAL-MOTOR DYSFUNCTION: Difficulties integrating from sensory intake to motor response in the same manner that the majority of people do.

PERSEVERATION: A repetitious response which is inappropriate to the given immediate situation. Perseveration is a sign that at the given moment the child perceives himself in a situation wherein he is threatened, in fear of failure, and/or with which he cannot cope if it is continued.

POSITION IN SPACE: Perception of the spatial relationship of an object to that of the observer.

PROPOSITIONALITY: The degree of volitional control or integration required for a given act. It varies inversely with the degree of habituation with which the individual performs the act.

RAPPORT: The interpersonal working relationship between individuals.

SET: The readiness to perform a task on the basis of predetermined rules. "Set" may function on two levels: (1) completion of the goal-directed act and (2) the maintenance of cognizance of the predetermined rules. Therefore the first level is a function of attention and the second level, an abstracting function.

SOMATIC: Pertaining to the body.

SOMATIC SENSATION: Sensory information about the body arising on, or from, the body via exteroceptors, proprioceptors (somesthesia).

SPASTICITY: A condition related to cortical brain damage, characterized by increased tone and sensitivity to stretch in one set of muscles in contrast to their antagonists.

SPATIAL RELATIONSHIPS: An ability of the observer to perceive the position of two or more objects in relation to himself and in relation to each other.

SPATIAL RIGIDITY: Not only refers to the child's need for spatial order in the environment because he cannot adequately function in clutter or environmental disorder but also includes the child's need to have objects in the environment in unvarying spatial relationship to one another.

STEREOGNOSIS: An ability to proprioceptively perceive objects, forms, materials, according to shape, size, quality of materials.

STRABISMUS: An eye condition in which there is lack of coordination of the eye muscles, characterized by a squint or cross eye.

STRUCTURING: Environmental control by the teacher or therapist so that stimuli perceived by the child and how he interprets such stimuli may be understood by the teacher or therapist.

TACTILE: Pertaining to touch or touch pressure.

TACTILE PERCEPTION: An ability to perceive tactile stimuli, to localize, discriminate, qualify, as in identification of form, shape, size, texture by touch pressure. (In many situations tactile and kinesthetic stimuli would be combined, as in manipulating an object.)

TEMPORAL RIGIDITY: The child's need for doing the same thing at the same time each day. It is the same as spatial rigidity as it refers to the time sequence of activities which hold importance or meaning for the child.

TRANSITION OR TRANSITIONAL ACTIVITIES: The need for closure is often so strong that the child in order to shift from one major task to another requires a "break" in addition to closure. Such intervening activity may be a physical movement from the part of the room where the first task was performed to another part of the room, or it may be a few minutes of gross motor activity.

VASOMOTOR LABILITY: A generalized instability of the child's homeostatic and vegetative functions, such as sudden flushing and/or pallor, sudden perspiration or "claminess" of the skin, highly unstable respiratory patterns or pulse rates. It may be a sign of subcortical brain damage or it may be an "early warning signal" of a potential catastrophic reaction.

VISUAL-MOTOR COORDINATION: An ability to coordinate movements of the body or with movement of a part or parts of the body with reference to visual input.

VISUAL-MOTOR SKILLS: Skills normally accomplished through visual perception and an integrated motor response or responses; often involve spatial relations and tactile perception; a kinesthetic perception is included, although not stated (manual skills).

VISUAL PERCEPTUAL DEVIANCE: Perceptual deviance in the visual sensory intake.

INDEX